MW00325209

Rhythm of the Tides

selected writings by Charles Sobczak

Also by Charles Sobczak:

Six Mornings on Sanibel *(1999)*
ISBN 0-9676199-5-5
$12.95

Way Under Contract, a Florida Story *(2000)*
ISBN 0-9676199-4-7
$14.95

Questions regarding ordering information and/or comments are encouraged and welcome via:

Toll Free Number:	877-472-8900
Local Number	941-472-0491
Fax Number:	941-472-1426
Email:	indigopress@earthlink.net
Web Address:	www.indigopress.net
Mailing Address:	Indigo Press, LC
	P.O. Box 977
	Sanibel Island, FL 33957

*This book is dedicated to
my wife Molly Heuer
and my two sons,
Logan and Blake.*

They are the true joy of my life.

☉

©2001 by Charles Sobczak

All rights reserved. No part of this book may be reproduced or transmitted in any form or by any means, electronic or mechanical, including photocopying, recording or by any information storage and retrieval system without written permission from the author, except by a reviewer who may quote brief passages in a review.

This is a first edition printing/September, 2001
Printed in the United States, in Naples, Florida

Published by: Indigo Press L.C.
              2560 Sanibel Boulevard
              Sanibel, FL 33957

You can contact us via the Internet at our web site: indigopress.net or by e-mailing us at indigopress@earthlink.net. For ordering information please call us toll free at 877-472-8900.

Rhythm of the Tides / by Charles Sobczak

ISBN 0-9676199-1-2

Cover photo by Charles Sobczak
Cover layout and design by Charles Sobczak and Bob Radigan

The cover photo was taken at sunset in Ding Darling National Wildlife Refuge on Sanibel Island, Florida. The photo was taken with a 300mm lens, manual focus, automatic exposure using 200 ASA Kodak film and a Nikon N-50 camera. The photograph was developed at Harmon Photography, 14330 S. Tamiami Trail, Ft. Myers, FL 33912

Acknowledgments

Over five years ago, Ted Kircher, then editor of the *Island Reporter*, asked if I would be interested in writing a weekly fishing column. Little did I realize that the fishing column would rekindle my passion for writing. Columns became novels. Novels that sold tens of thousands of copies. Novels that meant book signings, newspaper articles, speaking engagements, book festivals and the fulfillment of my lifelong dream of becoming an author. I cannot thank Ted Kircher enough.

I would also like to thank Jennifer Thomas, who works so hard on Indigo Press and whose dedication is beyond measure. My deepest appreciation and thanks go out to Kip Buntrock, who helps to keep these books on the bookshelves of the world. Of course, my deepest thanks and respect for Bob Radigan, my friend and talented graphic artist who designed the cover of this collection. He has once again astounded me with his instinct for design.

I have to thank all the members of the DP Society: Scott Martell, John and Nancy Jones, and the secret, honorary members. My appreciation and sympathies go out to the dutiful copy editors who have to tangle with my estranged sense of syntax. Those include Norm Ziegler, Sharon Heston, Ann Bellew, and Leanna Santo. Thank you once again for putting up with my notorious "their, there and they're," as always, used interchangeably and flippantly by yours truly.

But most importantly, I would like to thank the people who live and love this small barrier island called Sanibel. Your support and encouragement over the years have been wondrous. It is a village by the sea, filled with people who care about each other and the environment that surrounds them. Who exemplify an environmental awareness seldom found in the world. A dedication that has been an inspiration to me and a Godsend to the flora and fauna who share this stretch of sand and time along with us. Thank you for caring.

Table of Contents

To Catch a Catfish *(Cont.)*

Selected Tales *(1971-2001)*

Poetry *(1969-2001)*

Poetry *(cont.)*

Lyrics *(1973-1977)*   205

Author's Notes

This book is a journey - a personal voyage of words. From Zen poetry scrawled across the back of cheap napkins at Joe Huey's Chinese Restaurant at 2:00 a.m. in a caffeine induced delirium (circa 1969) in Duluth, Minnesota, to the epilogue from my last novel, *Way Under Contract*, this collection spans over three decades of my search for the perfect sentence. A search without resolve.

Selecting which tales, lyrics, poetry and essays to include herein and which to leave on the floor of the editing room was not an easy task. I sought to capture the essence of the time and space each piece was written in. From my early years back in college writing the *Universe Wisdom Lectures* to my current column in the *Islander*, I poured over a lifetime of writing in hopes of finding those works that still held the energy that was channeled into them years ago when the ink first spilled across sheets of empty paper.

Like most writers I have my personal favorites. Humorous stories that still hold laughter, sad tales written in tears and songs whose melodies reverberate through my life like a refrain I cannot let go of. Those are the works I chose. Those are the writings that make up this slim volume entitled *Rhythm of the Tides*.

All of the essays in the first two sections of this book were originally published in either the *Islander*, or the *Island Reporter* newspapers. Both of these papers are published weekly on Sanibel Island, Florida. Like the island they cover, their circulation varies from a sleepy 5,000 during the summer to a robust 10,000 during the busy winter tourist season. Sanibel Island lies along the southwestern edge of peninsular Florida. At its best, it's a village by the sea. At its worst, during the winter snowbird season, Sanibel is an overcrowded tourist town, not unlike Martha's Vineyard or Yellowstone in the summer. It is a good place to write.

I started my first column, *To Catch a Catfish*, in 1994 as a weekly series of "how to" fishing articles for the *Island Reporter*. Ted Kircher, presently a feature writer with *The Naples Daily News*, was the editor of the newspaper at the time and had asked me to give it a try. I had been a past president of the Sanibel Island Fishing Club and was known to have wet a line or two around the islands.

I accepted Ted's invitation and began writing. After a few years of penning detailed descriptions on tying dropper rigs for grouper, choosing the right Love lure colors for sea trout and a host of other "how to" articles, I found myself bored to tears with *To Catch a Catfish*. Shirlene Grasgreen, who sat at the front desk of the *Island Reporter's* office, was invariably the first person to read my weekly articles. She would always frown when she discovered that my submission that particular week was about fishing. With the encouragement of Shirlene and an increasing number of readers, I found my topics drifting further and further away from fishing.

Although many of the essays contained in this collection involve the sea in some way, they tend to be more philosophical than practical in nature. I soon found myself in the curious situation of writing a fishing column that had nothing to do with fishing. Shirlene, of course, was thrilled.

At the suggestion of Scott Martell, who was the executive editor of both newspapers at the time, we moved the column from the *Island Reporter* to the *Islander* in 1998. My new byline was called *The Sea and the Seashore*. With its new name, I was now given the green light to write about anything. My topics soon ran from blind men in the Grand Bazaar of Istanbul to the bike rides in Maine. The overriding theme being people and their relationships with their environment. A theme well loved on Sanibel as well as it is in the rest of the world.

In 1998, one of my columns, *Rhythm of the Sea*, won first place at the Florida Press Awards held in Daytona, Florida. The following year, in 1999, *The Trost Parcel* merited a second place award. At the suggestion of hundreds of readers, I decided to use my favorite columns as a basis for this compilation. For the most part, these essays are the same as when they were originally published. A few of them have been renamed, rewritten or expanded slightly from their original version. They no longer had to fit into the limited space of a newspaper format and, as an author, it was a joy to give them some additional room to run.

I plan to continue writing *The Sea and the Seashore*. But with the publishing of both novels, *Six Mornings on Sanibel* (1999) and *Way Under Contract, a Florida Story* (2000) and their unanticipated success, the frequency of the columns has fallen off. It has gone from a weekly to a monthly feature at best. The current editor of the *Islander*, Renny Severance, has been very understanding in this regard and I appreciate his patience.

My plans at present are to concentrate on the writing of my next novel. It is called *A Choice of Angels*. The story is based in Atlanta, Georgia and Istanbul, Turkey. It is a modern version of the often retold classic, *The Tragedy of Romeo and Juliet*. In *A Choice of Angels*, the son of a Baptist Pastor falls in love with the daughter of an Islamic merchant. They meet at a university in Atlanta. What follows is a tale of religious intolerance and the great human suffering it produces. The Capulets and the Montagues revisited once again, this time with a spiritual twist. The work should be completed within the next few years.

In the meanwhile, I hope you enjoy these modern parables and I appreciate all the tremendous support you have given me over the past few years. Indigo Press has received scores of wonderful cards, letters, e-mails and phone calls about the books and each and every comment is taken to heart and greatly appreciated. If you would like to contact us, call us toll free at 877-472-8900, or send us an e-mail at indigopress@earthlink.net.

Enjoy these tales and poems and thank you for taking a few hours of your precious time to give them a read.

Charles Sobczak
August, 2001

The Sea & The Seashore
(1998-2001)

I Could Learn To Love Kansas

*W*estern Kansas, where the great plains begin their slow, steady rise to the Colorado Rockies. On the open prairies, where the ceaseless wind charges across the semi-arid hills. Towns named Colby and Goodland, Scott City and Hays, Kansas. Villages where the layout is square and the county courthouse sits in the center, built stoutly of red clay brick and white pine trim. American vistas, with hometown cafés serving meatloaf and coconut cream pies. Hamburgers too thick to bite into.

Places where you know your neighbors. Where people still find the time to chit-chat down at the grain elevator, leaning against their Ford pickups discussing grain prices or that big tornado that ripped through Oberlin last month. Intimate and rural towns where your neighbors sometimes know more than they should.

I could learn to love living in Kansas. It's not a place I would choose to live - a land where the winter wheat is harvested by late June and the hills lie dusty brown and abandoned by August. No, it would have to be an environment that I was already familiar with. Had I been born there, or had my family moved to a farm near Wichita when I was just a boy. Terrains familiar to me. Winds that never abated. Winters cold and hostile.

I could imagine it all. Growing up in America's Great Plains. As a young boy with my crewcut friends, eagerly heading down to our favorite swimming hole on the Arkansas River in the heat of July. Or driving into Topeka with Mom and Dad twice a year for supplies, taking in a movie while we were there. Going to school in a small town K-through-12. Learning about the wonders of a world beyond the prairies.

Eventually falling in love with the Anderson girl. Settling down. Taking over her father's farm along with her two brothers, Jimmy and Brian. Good boys, the both of them.

Following the Kansas City Royals in the summer and cheering for the Denver Broncos in the fall. Hunting mule deer and shooting pheasants every autumn in the corn fields near Junction City. The rituals of life in the heartland, simple and inexorably linked to the earth.

It's like that for most of us in a way. We grow up, fall in love and live out our lives in our own private Kansas. Not that it was where we might have chosen to be born, but we never have that freedom - to choose where we arrive into our lives - do we?

We are all born into where we are and, in a way, into what we become. If we are born in Chicago or Alva, Albany or Stockton, we learn to love the Kansas that surrounds us. We see the wind gusts shimmering across the tall grasses like they were blowing across an ocean of auburn-tinted grain. Beautiful to us. Familiar.

All of which brings me to a conversation we had near the end of our journey that summer of 1997. My family and I were sitting around my sister Barb's kitchen table talking at length about our hometown: Duluth, Minnesota. In my family, all important conversations seem to begin and end around the kitchen table.

I had made a point that, of the six of us, none had stayed in Duluth. "It's just too damn cold and too hard a town to get by in," I added, as if summarizing my feelings toward the city of my distant youth.

My sister Barb, in her uncomplicated fashion, said that home is where the heart is. She went on to say that Duluth was a good town, full of fine people who were happy to be living there. Reflecting on what she had said for a minute, I nodded in agreement, remembering western Kansas. We live where we are, weaving the exquisite tapestry of friends and family from the fabric of life itself.

I could learn to love Kansas as easily as I've learned to love this remote barrier island called Sanibel. I could learn to love the rocky coastline of Nova Scotia or the cold, damp rain forests of Seattle. In the end, it is not the landscape that surrounds us that makes us who we are, but the landscape within. The landscape of the human heart.

Of Osprey Chicks And Children

*L*ate afternoon. The mid-winter sun slides effortlessly into the Gulf of Mexico on its eternal journey west. Shadows stretch and darken. The breeze dies and a dampened stillness settles over south Florida. Night is soon to follow.

The boys and I are over at the elementary school. We're throwing a bright orange frisbee to each other across the flat, grassy fields at the playground. A carefree game of discus, dropping our share of easy catches, missing any number of tosses, but no one is keeping score, and the score wouldn't matter even if someone ventured to keep it. It is not a contest. It is only a game.

Eventually, three other boys come over to join us. Seeing that the five of them want to play their own game, I graciously bow out, leaving them to that magic of laughter and shouting that boys are known for. Leaving them to each other, like five wolf cubs playing in an open field.

As I walked over to the bleachers to talk with some of the other parents at the fields that evening, it came to me. It was the sound of osprey chicks. High above the baseball diamonds and soccer fields, on nearly every other lighting tower, rested osprey nests. Carefully constructed nests of sticks and twigs that sat 70, to 80 feet in the air. Balanced on the top of long graceful towers made of aluminum and steel, placed there to light the fields below in the gathering darkness.

I could hear the young chicks clearly in the stillness of approaching nightfall: their high chirps followed by the arrival of one of their parents carrying a fresh mullet or a sea trout from Ding Darling National

Wildlife Refuge. Hungry chicks, with appetites not unlike my two sons. Sons who are always opening and closing our refrigerator in their relentless search for their own version of fresh mullet.

But it was more than that. It was a moment in time. A delicate, unexpected illumination. The two sounds, the shouts of the children playing and the chirps of the osprey families above, merged in the cool evening air, somehow becoming all the more transcendental for it. For the briefest of moments, they became one.

Suddenly we were sharing this same space and time. The birds in their element of feathers and air and the children in their element of soccer goals, frisbees and T-ball. Totally different, and yet totally the same. Sharing this home we call Florida. This state that is the fountain of youth.

This, I realized, is how it should be. A playground carved out of a 5,000 acre tract of wildlife preserve. A school surrounded by gumbo limbo trees, cabbage palms and patches of wild guava. Encircled by a natural ecosystem largely untouched by the industries of man. How rare and how vital.

Halfway between the bleachers and the five boys playing with their plastic saucer behind me, I stopped and stood in quiet wonder. My thoughts turned back several decades to Rachel Carson's *Silent Spring*. I remembered first reading her masterpiece of environmental awareness in high school. A high school surrounded by homes, streets and shopping centers.

Without Mrs. Carson's cry of alarm, those ospreys who soar on their long, pointed wings above me might not have made it through the heinous chemistry of DDT. That insecticide nearly wiped out many of our birds of prey: the bald eagle, the peregrine falcon and so many others. Like the tall, elegant metal poles that held the nests above me, DDT is an invention of man. A terrible invention.

I stopped and looked around. Every field was occupied by the children who live on this island, and some who came across the causeway from Fort Myers. They were all engrossed in their games and practices, probably unaware of the birds of prey soaring high above them. I knew, that as a parent, if one of them were to round third base and fall, his parents would quickly jump down from their bleacher and run to his rescue, tend to the bruise or the scrape, dress the scratches, if needed, and smother their child in love. It is what parents do.

But those cuts and wounds of childhood are immediate. They happen in an instant and are quickly followed by the cries of an injured child. No parent I know of could ignore those cries. How different that is from forever.

Because forever happens much more slowly. We used DDT for decades before Mrs. Carson sounded her desperate cry for help. But without the publication of *Silent Spring* in 1962, the gathering sky above might well be devoid of another flock of caring parents, parents who likewise tend to their young and share this moment in time. The osprey, the red-shouldered hawks, and the still rare southern bald eagle, might well have been lost.

Lost to the children below. Our children. Lost forever. Taken away by chemists in some lab built for profit. Designed to keep down the mosquitos in World War II and rid our fields of insects before the harvest. But what is the price of such a profit?

No, as I stood there as the cool night air wrapped around me, I became saddened by the thought of it. The thought that thus far our dominion over all the creatures of the Earth has amounted to little more than a long, unbroken series of extinctions. A twisted, unheroic charge if ever there was one. Species after species being brought to the edge of eradication, while thousands of others have already been pushed over that edge. Acre after hectare after square mile after entire ecosystems paved and plundered with scarcely a thought to the world we are handing to our children.

All done in the name of gross national product or progress or whatever the spin doctors of the modern world find politically correct. Fools the lot of us for believing them. As I stood there, amidst the chorus of these two animals, the children and the osprey chicks I decided to write this. Not that I, in all of my efforts, could do much to ensure that in 100, or 200 years from now this same symphony of species could be heard by some distant parent. Not I, nor you, nor any of us can make that promise. All we can do is do what we can do, today, tomorrow and forever. To tend to the needs of our children. All God's children.

My Raccoons

*I*t's taken me over a year to muster up the courage to write this column. One year of living with this silent anxiety, knowing that someone has to eventually break ranks and expose one of Sanibel's darkest secrets. Naturally I'm afraid of the retribution. Their usual tactics, garbage strewn all over my yard, the phone calls followed by those long silences. The inevitable hang up. Raccoon revenge at its finest.

Of course, I don't have any indisputable proof. But there is evidence everywhere, albeit circumstantial. Like the other night, coming home late after a DP Society meeting at the Bungalow. There were four of them, three adults and a young, teenage apprentice. The largest of the gang stood in the middle of my dark, dusty road and held his right paw out, stopping me dead in my tracks. They were working over my neighbor's high-security garbage bin. They had tools.

I just tightened my grip on the steering wheel and sat there shaking. There was nothing I could do. After using what appeared to be two tiny crowbars, they made off with a couple of hefty bags of trash and vanished into the surrounding woods. The big one gave me one long, cold stare before putting his paw down. His eyes flashed that deep, penetrating raccoon red. It was like a scene out of a Stephen King novel. It was more frightening than that. This wasn't the work of some horror novelist from Maine. These were wild animals within a few hundred feet of my house. These were my raccoons.

It's getting worse. Not that I haven't tried to stop them. A year ago I had so many bungee cords around my two plastic garbage cans that they looked more like a rubber band ball than trash containers. It didn't stop them. I heard them one night downstairs. They had broken into my tool shed, taking an extension cord and my Milwaukee Sawzall out to the motherlode. I can still hear the sound of that hacksaw blade slicing through those tightly stretched cords like they were made out of butter. They didn't even bother to put the extension cord away.

The next morning I was out there, coiling up my orange extension cord and picking up chicken bones, torn-open milk cartons and pieces of half-eaten tinfoil. Nothing remained inside my two trash cans except for that smelly, sticky stuff that is always at the bottom of garbage containers. Even new ones. The contents were everywhere, thrown around my yard as if dumped from a thousand yards high. They had taken my electric Sawzall with them.

Maybe I'm getting too paranoid. Maybe I'm wrong about the mob connection, the Italian last names. But of this much I'm dead certain: Sanibel's raccoons can read. They also know how to use tools and I'm quite confident that they can hack into your computer, given half a chance. That's why I'm writing this column. I'm risking everything to uncover one of the island's best kept secrets. These aren't your normal, cute little Midwestern raccoons down here; these are the elite of the species. They are trained dumpster divers, capable of picking padlocks, undoing complex knots and using the Internet in their search for an old Bailey's bag full of tasty trash.

Ask any of the local restaurant owners if you have any doubt. A few weeks ago I noticed that one of them has gone to extreme measures in an effort to keep the little varmints from getting to his leftover buffalo wings. Two-by-fours, oversized bungee cords, even cinder blocks on the lids, and all to no avail. The raccoons prevailed, using a complex system of ropes, pulleys and prying tools to gain access to their greasy prize. They were behaving more like a group of freshmen at MIT than a dozen furry mammals looking for a free lunch.

The Sanibel Police stay out of it. They've been warned. The City Council, the Planning Department, all of them would rather take on the good-ole boys of Lee County than mess with the island's raccoons. No one wants to stand up to them. No one wants to talk about the disappearing handguns, the stolen Island Locksmith van or the missing dynamite. It's worse than imaginable.

So, this might be my last column. But someone had to spill the beans, even at the risk of being lashed to one of those cinder blocks and being found a month later beneath the high span of the causeway. Someone had to go state's evidence and turn informant about this mutant strand of super-intelligent bandits working the island's midnight shift. I know what's coming.

They'll find this issue of the Islander in a week or two. Probably wrapped around some delicious fish heads or covered in cockatiel droppings and bird seed, but they'll find it nonetheless. After reading it, they'll be looking for me. They'll make it look like an accident. They always do.

In the meanwhile, keep at it. Like an endless game of chess against a Russian grand master, keep trying to keep them out of your garbage cans. Bigger bungee cords, sturdier containers, anything to make it to next Tuesday's weekly pick up. It's too late for me. I'm done for.

Wait a minute, I think I hear something downstairs...

A Blind Man Selling Crazy Glue

*I*t was in the Grand Bazaar, an endless maze of small covered shops in the old city of Istanbul, where I met him. Molly and I were weaving in and out of a handful of the 4,000 shops in that labyrinth of tiny stores looking for gifts for friends and family. It was crowded. The Grand Bazaar in Istanbul is always crowded.

While Molly was bargaining with some Turkish merchants over a copper platter, he walked up to me. His white cane was nothing more than a four-foot piece of half-inch PVC pipe. He wore an old gray woolen sports coat, with pants that didn't match and a brown flannel hat in the style that mobsters used to wear. Underneath the sports coat was a tired wool sweater and below that you could make out the faded, pilled collar of an ancient T-shirt. He was an older Turk, maybe 60 - his hair graying, his dark skin deeply etched and the teeth behind his wonderful smile worn and yellowed.

He was also blind. There could be no mistaking that. Unlike the blind here in America, he wore no dark sunglasses to cover his eyes. When he looked toward your voice, his right eye would remain closed, but his left eye would open just wide enough to allow you to see that it could not see. It was a faded blue and it lacked any sign of a pupil. It was the eye of a blind man.

As he shuffled through the crowd he carried a small plastic bag in his right hand, holding his white PVC cane with his left. When he approached the shop I was standing outside of, several clerks came out to greet him. They called him by some Turkish name I cannot recall and went into a short but enthusiastic conversation with him in a language incomprehensible to me.

The blind man smiled and responded in conversation. You could see that he was a regular in the Bazaar. They knew him, and he, in kind, obviously knew their voices.

It was just after their brief exchange when I asked one of the merchants who spoke a little English what he was doing here in this crowded bazaar. The young Turkish man kept saying that he sells "clue." I didn't understand the mis-pronunciation. Seeing that I was confused, the young peddler reached into the blind man's plastic bag and took out a tube to show me. It was glue, the kind that comes in those small tin tubes, a generic form of Krazy glue.

It was then that I realized that the old blind man walks around the massive Grand Bazaar selling tiny tubes of crazy glue to who ever needs it. Two tubes for a million Turkish lira, which, due to their 56% a year inflation, is worth about 90 cents U.S. But the insanity of his enterprise is what struck me. There are only four bills printed in Turkey. The ten-million lira, worth about nine dollars U.S., the one-million, the five-hundred thousand and the two-hundred and fifty-thousand note lira. The smallest denomination being a piece of printed paper worth less than a quarter. They are all the same size and the same texture. A blind man would have absolutely no way of knowing which bill he was getting.

Although I had no immediate need for them, I decided to purchase two tubes from the old man. The other merchants smiled as I did. I thought to myself, this is completely absurd. How can you have a blind salesperson? Anyone could hand him a lessor denomination bill and effectively buy the crazy glue at the ridiculous price of eight tubes for a million lira. Eight tubes for 90 cents. Surely the blind man must have known that he could so easily be taken advantage of. Assuredly everyone in the bazaar was aware of the irony.

But I purchased them regardless, and slipped both small tubes into my pocket as Molly finished her haggling with the other clerk over the platter. The old man continued on, shuffling blindly down another of the endless corridors that make up this ancient covered market.

Without giving it another thought, I smiled. That was the whole point. For in fact, we are all blind men selling crazy glue. We are all vulnerable. Selling our skills and our wares in a world filled to overflowing with con-men and unscrupulous buyers. Cheats and scoundrels, corporations and companies, all of them more than willing to take advantage of us.

There are the other moments, of course... The times when we are the ruthless buyer, or the shameless employer, seizing an opportunity to take more than our fair share. Insider trading or unfairly exploiting another human being.

It dawned on me that every transaction involves more than the product changing hands and the money passing across a counter. It involves a trust. A trust unspoken that says the price is fair and no one is getting short-changed in the process. You can lie, mislead, pull a fast one, steal, and fudge, but it never matters to the blind man selling crazy glue. Because, in the end, it is never about cheating a blind man. It is only about cheating yourself.

Walking With Papa

*K*ey West has a style of night, spinning the moist ocean atmosphere around you like a black cocoon, silky and tropical. The evenings implore you, no, they beg you to come out and inhale their intoxicating air. And this small, island village has much to offer to a midnight wanderer, where the din of Duval contrasts sharply with the quiet side streets. Quaint, endearing streets made cavernous below a canopy of dark-skinned limbs and green, waxy leaves. Exotic trees - mahoganies and generous live oaks stretching over the streets in the thick, oceanic aura of an island in the sea.

After a long day of fishing the Gulf Stream, the three of us, David, the Captain and I took turns showering and headed into the warm, inviting darkness of Key West. Still unshaven, we bounced in and out of the bars that line Duval between T-shirt shops and overpriced restaurants. We were thirsty. The rum and cokes tasted wonderful amidst this newfound ocean of people we were now fast upon.

The crazy college boys from Iowa chasing skirts like the big bull dolphin in the Gulf Stream did earlier that day. The fresh tans on the women, accented by bright, floral dresses, cleanly shaven legs and the faint scent of sexuality. The laughter and the flirting of girls on holiday. The sound of reggae music slipping down the crowded streets, putting a rhythm into the strides of the tourists and locals alike. A night on the town.

We were drinking hard. Everyone, except a few stalwart shopkeepers and the local police, was drinking hard. It was the perfect thing to do on a raucous Saturday night.

David and the Captain wanted to go into a local strip joint. I was already too drunk to object. The dancer was young and beautiful, moving with the grace of a female leopard. But I soon became bored with her tireless undulations and wandered out into the wild, late night alone, wanting to be alone for a while.

I was drunk when I met him. As drunk as roses. He was standing just outside his favorite bar, looking pissed off. Key West had become a tourist town and you could tell that he was disappointed.

"I thought that I might run into you out here," I said as I approached.

"Yeah, I thought so too," he replied.

"You don't like it, do you?"

"No. I don't."

"It was inevitable," I tried to explain, weakly defending the mayhem surrounding both of us. "Its native charm was its own undoing. The gingerbread architecture, the distant scent of Havana, the end of Highway One. It had to happen eventually. There isn't anything that you or I can do about it."

"No, you're probably right." He reluctantly conceded. The topic was closed. We had far more important things to talk about. We had stories of the sea to share, and the way he last looked at Catherine.

We walked and walked, our conversation spilling late into the night like a liquid mythology. I had a small pint of rum with me. We took turns taking slugs off of it. It felt good to be talking about the dreams we shared but it was the differences that intrigued him the most.

"Everything has changed," I told him. "The world has collapsed into itself. You can't just go around killing things any longer. There are simply not enough wild animals left. Safaris are now done with 400 mm lenses and not .40-caliber bullets. The world is a million times smaller, defined by www.coms and satellite telephones.

"And the Gulf Stream isn't as blue as it was back then, when the old man played out his big fish. It's tainted with the blood of a thousand refugees and darkened with the oil of an endless stream of super tankers. Huge ships going from one place to another carrying barrels and barrels of nada."

He said that if this were true, then it wasn't a world for him any longer. He said that maybe the shotgun was the right thing to do after all. Hearing him talk like that broke my heart. I didn't know what to say.

As he walked back into his cut coral house just off Whitehead, past the six-toed cats and through the teak door, I hesitated. The big, wrought iron gate was locked. I just stood there and realized how drunk I was, and just how sobering the truth is.

The machismo of Papa is dead, killed in a planet filled with too many people and no real definition. No Franco to fight against, no great fish left to fight. Just questionable democracies and drift nets the length of Cuba. The brave new world was just a huge corporation with no one in it who was responsible for anything. Heroes were rare, displaced by carjackers and terrorists with enigmatic agendas too difficult to decipher. Bad things happened and the local news covered it. Covered it in blood-red color, running the good footage twice. Always in slow motion.

As I leaned against the metal gate outside the house, next to the sign that posted the hours and the cost of admission to Hemingway's old home, three of the cats came up to me. They approached cautiously at first, then, as they realized that I meant them no harm, each one let me pet it. It was great to finally talk to him.

I stumbled my way back to Duval, looking for the strip joint. David introduced me to his new, fresh squeeze. It was the young stripper. She looked odd wearing a brightly colored sun dress. We all made tipsy, mindless conversation and wandered back towards the hotel to retire.

It was very late. Key West has a way with darkness. The bulls will run next year. There is hope that America will find itself again. Someday. He knows that. He always has.

The Touron Phenomenon

*M*id-March. The rental cars back up five miles to the Sanibel
School on their way off-island in the late afternoon. Every
one of the passengers just had lunch at the Bubble Room, or was it the
Mucky Duck? The traffic creeps eastward almost imperceptibly, like
a long, metallic glacier engineered in Detroit. Periwinkle Way looks
like a rental car lot with all the inventory accidently left in idle. It's the
height of the tourist season, the perfect time to observe the touron
phenomenon.

It's certainly not unique to Sanibel, although we seem to suffer
from an acute form of it during our so called 'peak season.' Symptoms
include the following:

You are driving down Periwinkle when you notice that the
enormous white Cadillac directly in front of you has stopped cold in
the middle of the road. You hit the brakes. The 14,000-pound garbage
truck behind you squeals to a halt not four inches from your rear
bumper. Then the phenomenon happens.

The driver of the Cadillac, whom you assumed was having a
stroke, or at the very least some unexpected mechanical failure, slowly
winds down his window, pulls out a disposable camera, and takes a
quick snap of the Old Pirate Playhouse. You look in your rear view
mirror one last time to verify the fact that you nearly died for this tourist
to take a hurried shot with a cheap plastic camera in the middle of
Periwinkle. You roll your eyes in disbelief.

Or this one. You are taking some friends through Ding Darling
and as luck would have it, you encounter a rare American crocodile

sunning itself near the very end of the drive. The five-hundred pound crocodile is just off the edge of Wildlife Drive, not ten feet from where a conscientious volunteer has quickly strung one of those bright yellow tapes to keep the visitors from getting too close. The kind of tape you see at crime scenes.

As you are getting out of the car, you hear the volunteer yelling at some 13-year-old girl who has ducked under the tape and started down the embankment toward the croc.

"Stop!" He shouts in a moment of panic. "What on earth are you doing?"

Luckily she stops. This dinner-sized girl comes back behind the crime scene tape. You overhear her explaining to the unraveled docent why she was going down to touch the crocodile.

"I wanted to touch it because my girlfriend said it was made out of plastic. Is it?"

"Is it made out of plastic? Are you asking me if that 11-foot crocodile is made out of plastic? The answer is no, it's very real and not at all reluctant to grab you if you get too close."

"But it doesn't move," adds the young lady, trying to give some credibility to her suicide mission.

Just then the croc drops its deadly jaws closed and the crowd responds with ohhhs, and ahhhs. You can hear the teenager saying to her friend, "I told you it wasn't plastic."

"But those pink flamingos back at the lookout were," her friend insists. They were spoonbills.

The volunteer mumbles the word "morons" to himself as he watches the teenagers get back into their minivan with their parents. The croc is mildly disappointed. She's always wanted to know what one of those things tastes like.

The stories are endless. Little old ladies who won't come out of their rented house because, quote, "It's surrounded by baby alligators," which turn out to be harmless lizards. Cars pulled over blocking the bike path reading maps of Cape Coral or Marco Island. Dazed, confused tourists everywhere, armed with scores of those throwaway cameras and twenty-dollar travelers checks.

It's called the touron phenomenon: 50 percent tourist, 50 percent moron. Hence the term: touron. Starting in March and ending the week of Easter we have an abundance of them. Well-meaning tourists on vacation. Clueless and happy to be in the Sunshine State. Sending postcards north by the boxcar load.

Just remember last summer when you were in Martha's Vineyard...or was it Yellowstone? Remember when you stopped your car on Highway 401 to take that perfect shot of a bull elk, or that sunset in Monterey? You instantly became one: a touron. It's a human equation that states emphatically that whenever a local strays over fifty miles from their home turf they reduce their ability to drive, read maps or make intelligent decisions by fifty percent. Some might argue that the number's closer to ninety-five percent. We no longer know the back way, or east from west, or up from down for that matter. We become tourons.

So the next time you're stalled at a four-way stop with three tourons, sit back, relax and enjoy it. Turn up the radio and listen to "All Things Considered" for an hour or so while the bedazzled eyes of the three lost tourists dart from one to another to another all trying to decide who's going to pull out first. Behaving as though this is the first four-way stop they have ever experienced.

Acting like tourons, just like we acted when we were in their hometown last summer. March on Sanibel Island, Florida. The weather's been great, hasn't it?

Passion

*T*he image echos through my life like the melody of a song I cannot forget. The camera rises slowly as Zorba and his "boss" dance on the beach below as that frenetic bouzouki plays on. Their precarious plans to carry the freshly cut timber down to the shoreline have just collapsed in ruin, the boss is now broke and the monks up on the mountaintop are in a panic while Anthony Quinn, playing Zorba, says, "Let's dance, Boss." That is passion. Let's dance.

It is a zest for life, a commitment to a dream, a hobby or a goal that supercedes the mundane. It is one of the most difficult edges to walk and because of that, one of the most rewarding. We envy those who have it. We all know someone who does. There is a sparkle in their eyes that betrays them. A fire in their soul.

It is easier to describe through the works of those who embody the very heart of passion. Artists and writers, environmentalists and great leaders who exemplify what it is to live life to the fullest.

It is seen clearly in the sensual brush strokes of Vincent Van Gogh. I cannot look at the stars on a windy night and not see *Starry Night*. A painting of Van Gogh's room hangs in my office, reminding me of the need to live life with intensity, with passion.

There are others who have shown us how it is done: Roosevelt, Mandela, Aretha, Picasso, John Muir, Hemingway, King, the list is endless. What all of them share is a singular focus, an ability to envision their dreams and pursue them through to the end. Men and women to whom failure is only a momentary stumbling block on their way up to the mountaintop. They don't live life, they grab life.

All of us have this ability. Be it a passion for shelling or philosophy. Up at dawn, flashlight in hand, scouring the empty beach in search of some elusive mollusk, or reading Sartre at midnight, searching for an explanation. Be it for traveling, or reading, fishing or watercolors, all of us have the potential to partake in the sheer exhilaration of finding our personal passions. And we should follow those dreams.

Because with passion we find meaning. Along with this focus comes an element of clarity. Life becomes richer, the colors more intense, the moments more precious. With passion the human experience is more fulfilled, more alive. Without it, life can quickly become stale.

But there is a cost. Van Gogh's ear and Hemingway's shotgun remind us of this. The price tag becomes apparent the instant passion overwhelms us and inexplicably refuses to release us from its grip. It is the dark side of the equation, the Hitlers, the lunatics and the suicide bombers of the world. It happens without warning. It is the moment when the vision becomes all encompassing. We suddenly realize that there is no clear way out. It is the price of passion at its worst. It is the intensity taken too far, the individual's will turned loose upon the fields of human madness.

It is a balancing act. Walking along the edge of what we love to do and knowing when to resist its seductive invitation. Knowing when the voice becomes the song of the sirens, calling us into the rocks of self-absorption. No one but you knows when that moment is, but the knowledge of it must never be allowed to fade.

Henry David Thoreau once wrote that, "The mass of men lead lives of quiet desperation." It is a quote I have never forgotten. Unfortunately, it is still true far too often. It doesn't have to be.

Take hold of something, anything, and dive in. Be it a golf club, a tennis racket, a paint brush, a pen or a model airplane. Become possessed, enthralled, captivated by the magic of the moment. Life is so much richer and far more beautiful for it. Passion. Search your heart and find it. When you do, let's dance.

The Sound Of Tinsel Falling

*W*e stopped and sat at the top of the stairs, our little fingers wrapped tightly around the banister, our anticipation beyond measure. Christmas morning, 1958. Peggy, David, Stevie and I paused for a moment at the top of the stairs, looking over a living room bursting with the sights and smells of Christmas. The colored lights flashing on the tree, the aroma of a fresh-cut spruce, the strands of tinsel dancing from the warm air rising off the radiator. And the presents, sprawled beneath the tree in brightly colored wrappings. Our presents.

We were frozen there, the four of us, as if suspended in time. As frozen as the snow and ice that held northern Minnesota captive that morning some 40 years ago. We were waiting for Mom to get her robe on and come down to help us cut off all the bows and ribbons, ripping into that thin, decorative paper in a flurry of joy.

For the moment, we were silent and still, transfixed by the postcard scene below us. Mesmerized by the round, silver ornaments and the strings of popcorn and cranberries that spiraled up the evergreen. A panorama culminating in that dimestore angel perched precariously at the very top of that seven-foot pine.

What if that angel was watching the four of us? Watching our dark brown eyes sparkle from the reflection of the Christmas lights. Seeing us shiver a little, chilled from sitting on the cold wooden stairs in our pajamas because there wasn't any time to get dressed that distant, frosty morning. The sun was still lumbering along, spilling its slanted light on upper Michigan when Stevie and I awoke. We were unable to wait any longer. Unable to get back to sleep.

What a tableau that Woolworth's angel would have witnessed. Peggy barely three years old, and the three boys, each of us just a few years apart. The huge wooden stereo console sitting in the hallway just below us with the coat rack standing beside it. The floor covered in a floral print linoleum and the sound of our old refrigerator humming in the kitchen.

America in the '50s. Eisenhower was president. The cars parked outside were shaped like rocket ships with tall, stylized fins and a surplus of chrome. Out, across the American landscape, rows of tract houses going up in a booming suburban landscape. A blue-collar America, with industrial dreams and a future made cloudy only by the distant threat of communism. Post-war, post-depression America with a future as bright as those multicolored Christmas bulbs flickering beneath us.

We didn't pause on that stairway for long. As soon as Mom's slipper hit the landing above us, we bolted toward the living room as though a dam full of children had just given out. We tumbled down the stairway and spilled across the floor in a cascade of excitement.

"Which present's mine?" "Whose gift is this, the name tag's been torn off?" A few minutes later, and it was over. We were busy playing with our Tinker Toys, train sets and dolls. The rest of the day would melt away into a belated breakfast, a sumptuous turkey dinner and an early bedtime. I wish it could always be that simple.

Dad started drinking a few years later and then came the divorce. The presents thinned. The myth of Santa Claus was killed in some grade school hallway by a mean-spirited kid who wanted you to grow up. "Grow up Chuckie, there ain't no such thing as Santa Claus."

Innocence lost. Kennedy's assassination in 1963 cut through the heart of the post-war American dream like a vision imploding onto itself. Faith soon shattered below the discord of the '60s. The race riots and Martin Luther King's murder soon followed. Bobby's death came next and the polarizing war in Vietnam continued without an end in sight. Napalm and stretchers filled with wounded young men dominated the evening news. Some of the young men in those stretchers were bleeding from Vietcong gunfire, some from the Ohio National Guard.

The mean spirited kid in the hallway might have well been saying, "Grow up Chuckie, there ain't no such thing as democracy, justice or equality." Perhaps he was right.

The road continues. Adulthood brings you down its crooked highway in an endless litany of lost myths. You see divorces, treachery, deceit and insanity walking alongside you and soon learn there is little or nothing you can do about it. You come to terms with the ways of the world as you come to terms with yourself. The moment on the stairway becomes a distant memory. It is the sound of tinsel falling, a silence in our souls that bear sad witness to the loss of childhood. The loss of innocence.

But I will not leave you with that. I will not leave you with a world filled with impeachment hearings and all the grim disclosures in the hallways of this vicious world. That wouldn't be fair. By now, both of us know that corruption and evil are out there. That it is a part of our world and that it will never change. We cannot deny it. But we can forgive it.

We can do what is right with what has been so graciously gifted to us. We can share what we have with those less fortunate and love whom we love with all our hearts. We can stop and remember our moments on that stairway 20, 40, or was it 60 years ago.

That Christmas morning when we were eight years old. When it was you who beheld that shimmering tree, or that glowing Menorah in the living room. When we still believed in Santa Claus. Because deep in our hearts we will always believe in Santa Claus, won't we?

Have a wonderful holiday this year with your friends and family and remember to show that dimestore angel that your sparkle is still there...that life can be wonderful, and that faith will find victory in this world of sad and lonely souls.

The Bugs Have Won

*T*here is no way to break this news to you politely. Not at this juncture. We have all been in denial about the crisis for centuries, probably longer. It's called human nature, that wretched combination of self-importance and refusing to look too closely at the evidence. Some call it denial. But the evidence is overwhelming in this instance: The bugs have won.

I've been wrestling with this column for weeks on end, trying to decide how to break the news to you without giving anyone cause to write those nasty "letters to the editor" responses that the local papers thrive on. You know the type; "While reading Mr. Sobczak's column last week, I found that he was totally without..." The rest goes without saying.

But as it is, there is no avoiding the issue at this point, no hedging. The truth is out there and the truth is that the insects are the unanimous victors. They rule the earth and they rule it with stingers, pinchers, allergic rashes and bites. As much as we might consider ourselves the crowning achievement of the last hundred million years of biological evolution, from their perspective, which is far and away more realistic, we are what we are: fodder and hosts.

Let's start with the least innocuous of them, the benign sugar ant. My mother-in-law owns what I would call one of the island's generic gulf-front condominiums along the beach. On paper that is. For the past 20 years she has fought a losing battle with sugar ants. Short of using plastic explosives, which are not allowed per the condominium docs, she has tried everything to rid her kitchen of these tiny, harmless insects.

To no avail. Chemicals, traps, herbal remedies, sprays, adhesives and poisons have all been thrown at these tiny little six-legged creatures. Over those decades, although many a battle has been won to those light red ants, the war is theirs. They always come back. A week after the fumigation and they're there, making a beeline to the toaster crumbs with a newfound sense of toxic resistance. At this point, my mother-in-law is considering leaving cookies and honey out for them at night like you might a stray cat. A six-legged stray cat slightly larger than a pinhead. It's easier.

Moving up the ladder but down in size, we come to a Florida favorite: the no-see-um. Who invented this one? Here's a bug that you can't even see without having two pairs of reading glasses on, that is capable of going through any screening short of solid sheets of black plastic (which do obscure the view from your lanai, by the way), and seems to thrive in all given climactic conditions.

That ability is borne out repeatedly by comments heard at the island post office. Remarks like, "It's been dry lately, and, well, those darn no-see-ums love it when it's dry." Or, "We've been getting a lot of rain on the island this past week, and, you know, those nasty no-see-ums love that rain." OK, which is it? Dry? Wet? From the beach to the mangroves and everywhere in between, the island's no-see-um population rules. Invisible flying teeth finding delight and nourishment in an endless stream of bipedal food flown down here fresh weekly from places like Dayton and Syracuse. Along with their tan, these tourists return with a plethora of bumps and itches, living in complete denial about the fact that they were a walking buffet table the entire week they were here on Sanibel.

But the list is extensive and my allotted column inches far too insufficient. Try two hundred and forty species of ants alone living in the State of Florida; eighteen species of termites; hundreds of species of wasps, hornets and bees; dozens of roaches, centipedes, millipedes, spiders, lice, midges, fleas, and biting flies. Billions and billions of predators just waiting for you to head outside for a lazy afternoon outing. There are, in fact, five million insects for every person living on Earth. How's that for odds?

Although I realize it would decimate Florida's prolific real estate industry, I long for the day when developers are required to call their new projects in the Sunshine State names that more accurately represent their locales. I've always thought it ironic that at golf courses named "Hawk's Ridge," there are never any hawks nor, in this flat, unbroken plain of south Florida, are there any ridges. Why not call the new development what it is, "Mosquito Swale Estates." How about "Termite Woods" Let's try "No-See-Um Shores." The gates in front of that exclusive subdivision might keep out the riff-raff, but they do little to halt the deluge of bugs that have graciously sublet this stretch of swamp to the developers. The fact remains, it wouldn't look right on their full-color brochures and, as usual, everyone is in denial.

No, the bugs have won. They've become pesticide-resistant, they've outlasted a million species of mammals, birds and dinosaurs over the millennia and their future looks better than promising. It looks fabulous.

Even if you decide to write that nasty letter to the editor about the topic and tone of this column, when you go out to put the envelope in your mailbox, chances are that a dozen fire ants will make quick work of your sandal-covered feet. You're better off staying inside, closing up your doors and windows and having a good cry. Sorry about writing this ugly exposé after you've booked your vacation or purchased that nice piling house in the swamp, but the guilt was getting to me.

There, I feel better already. What's that little dark thing I see bolting across the bathroom floor out of the corner of my eye? Could it be a cockroach? Face it, the bugs have won.

That Downhill Run

*W*ere that life was as flat as Florida. As uninterrupted as the
Everglades, broken only by the occasional rise of a
hardwood hammock, or the fall of some tidal river carving itself deep
into the sawgrass. Or, at its worst, no more than the green, rolling hills
near Ocala. Long gentle slopes followed rhythmically by long gentle
inclines. Stands of sprawling live oak with well-groomed chestnut
thoroughbreds standing in their shade. A portrait of beauty in repose.
Were that it was so.

Which takes us to Maine and how I found this parable. Northern
Maine, up near the northeastern tip of the United States, in Acadia
National Park. There, on the 100-year-old carriage trails carved beneath
the Bubble Mountains, I learned a lesson not soon forgotten. I learned
the truth about those downhill runs.

We, Molly, the boys and I, were up in Maine on vacation that
summer, staying in a town called Blue Hill, visiting with some good
friends. While there, we decided to take an afternoon and head to Bar
Harbor to rent some bicycles and enjoy a few miles of the carriage trails
that wander through the park. I ended up with one of those child
attachments behind me, hauling little Sarah, our friends' daughter, behind
me. She was only seven and we felt that the steep hills along the way
might prove too demanding for her.

It was the right decision. Maine is not Florida. The granite hills
that make up Acadia rise steeply from the deep fiords below. The
carriage trails, even though they were designed to be as level as possible,
were a far cry from the bike paths of Sanibel. Here, on this low-lying

barrier island, the only hills that can be found are the rare bridges crossing the occasional freshwater sloughs.

On Mount Desert Island, the hills are long, steep and arduous. With little Sarah peddling as hard as she could, there were times when the only solution to the steepest hills was to dismount and walk the bicycle. If we had enough momentum going into the climb, we might make it halfway up the next hill before our steam ran out. That's when it came to me.

That the carriage trails of Acadia and life have much in common. As Sarah and I would laugh together, coasting down a long, pine-shadowed trail, we both knew what was next. Sarah would sometimes acknowledge it in her sweet, tiny voice saying, "We're going to pay for this, Charlie. We're going to have to pay."

And pay we did. Because at the end of every long, downhill glide, came another hill. This time it went up rapidly and gravity, whose generosity we had so enjoyed, now turned on us like a junkyard dog. It was payback time.

It dawned on me that moment that this bike ride was not unlike the journey that is life. That life is a series of downhill glides and uphill struggles. That it is never as flat as south Florida, no matter how hard we wish it were so.

No, it is a sojourn of unexpected hills and, if we're lucky, long, enchanting valleys. Sometimes, for no apparent reason, the hills become mountains. Mountains that seem only to rise. They rise as quickly as the Tetons, or the Andes. They stretch upward as mercilessly as the Himalayas. Inclines steep and treacherous, filled with sorrows, setbacks and pain. Lives that are played out along a bike path that has no downhill stretches. Hard lives, full of tragedies and heartache.

We all know someone whose life seems to be stuck on one of these hard-fought trails. Someone who has seen too much uphill, too much suffering, and too much pain. All we can do to help is to take their heavy bikes from them for a while and help them push them along their journey, praying that they might find a stretch of downhill glide along the way. Help them however we can.

Then there are the fortunate ones. The people who purchased Microsoft as a penny stock, who stay happily married, and who never seem to encounter any but the smallest of slopes along the way. We all have met a few people like this along life's voyage. The lucky ones, the ones who seem to live charmed existences.

But for the most of us, the trail will be long and varied. We will have those trying moments in life, exhausted and wanting to give up. But we will eventually reach the top of that next steep hill, and, once there, we will see the valley beyond. We will get back on our bikes, smile and start that next long downhill glide.

The glide that makes it worthwhile. The wind on our face, our lives coasting down a beautiful forest path on a summer's day in northern Maine. Friends in front of us and friends not far behind us. A moment in time, with the sun casting long shadows across the trail and the sound of seagulls heard above the green canopy of an ancient forest. All the while with little Sarah tagging behind us as we end our downhill run saying, "We're going to have to pay for this, Charlie."

Indeed we are. Indeed we do. But it's worth it.

Original Innocence

"For it is in giving that we receive."

St. Francis of Assissi

*I*t was long ago. So long ago that I can no longer recall the name of the movie. It was an obscure film, not the kind you would find playing at your local Cinema 20 on a weekend night. It was too aesthetic, too obtuse.

The movie was about the life of St. Francis of Assissi. For those of you unfamiliar with St. Francis, he founded the Franciscan Order of Friars Minor in 13th century Europe. He is also known as the patron saint of ecologists and animals. Some, including myself, consider him to be a prophet, a visionary.

What I remember most about the film was a scene near the end of the movie. At the time, St. Francis was causing quite a stir throughout Italy. He had forsaken all earthly wealth. He and his followers were roaming the medieval countryside in rags, preaching obedience, poverty and devotion to Christ. They were helping lepers and the poor, treating prince and pauper, wildlife and countrymen with equal respect. The Holy Mother Church, which ruled Western civilization at the time, was not impressed.

The Pope had called St. Francis to Rome to admonish him and his followers for their eccentric behavior. The camera angles were from high above the marble floor of St. Peter's Basilica as Francis of Assissi walked toward the most powerful man on earth in those dark, mysterious days of 13th century Europe. St. Francis was all but naked.

He looked so vulnerable. His hair was long and a thick beard covered his face. His feet were dirty and his body was worn thin by months of fasting and living in abject poverty. In juxtaposition to this emaciated Saint stood the well-fed Papal entourage, dressed in embroidered robes and fine, hand-sewn garments of the finest linens.

When St. Francis and his small group of followers finally made it to the foot of the altar, Pope Innocent III stood silent. He knew in an instant that this poor, wretched-looking man that stood before him was not to be admonished, but admired. The Pope gazed down at St. Francis, looked up and across the crowd of cardinals, priests and clerics that had come to witness this rare encounter and said something that I will never forget.

"We must all remember that before original sin there was original innocence."

How true. Before the fall from grace in the Garden of Eden a thousand, thousand sins ago, we were all innocent. Like St. Francis, we could stand in that garden and the song birds and mourning doves would light upon our shoulders. There was a time when we didn't have an unspoken distance between the natural world and ourselves. We were a living part of the earth, intimately linked to the rhythms of our surrounding ecosystems.

Now, as it was in that late medieval Europe, we live in a world severed from nature. We live in a society filled with the tyranny of mankind; the injustices, the senseless wars, and the endless layers of corruption. This is why it is so important to remember our native virtue - that in all of us, somewhere, lies not the heart of darkness that the evening news would soon lead us believe, but the heart of innocence. We can do good things, and when these good things are done, we owe it to ourselves to celebrate our original innocence. In doing so, we find faith.

Not the faith we equate with religious zealots. That faith is oftentimes too superficial and too rarified to embrace. The greater faith is that which we have in each other. It is an unwavering willingness to accept the premise that we, you and I, are inherently good. It is seeing not the man who has committed the crime, but the shattered child within that man. It is the faith of forgiveness and compassion. A faith in life and the knowledge that time will allow us to decipher the larger metaphor contained within the worst moments of our lives.

When we can accept this, which is somewhat like trying to hold an ocean in the palm of your hand, the rest of the enigma makes perfect sense. I am not talking logical sense, or that box canyon that is Aristotelian reasoning, but a far, far deeper sense. A sense of surrender to the mystery of existence.

Because it is a mystery after all. So great and so complex a miracle is our life that most of the time we simply choose not to think about it. We know that the universe is infinite and that we had no choice in the decision of our own consciousness, but there is little we can do but accept the terms of the puzzle without reservation. We are because we are.

That is where faith comes in. It trumps the banality of sheer existence. But there is a caveat. When you give of yourself, your time, your worldly things, your love and your compassion, you cannot do so with the expectation of receiving anything in return. Ever. You must surrender unilaterally. You must, like a school kid in the great recess of existence who is getting beat up by the proverbial seventh grade bully, simply say "uncle," and throw in the towel. And why not?

Once you surrender you find yourself anew on this glorious field of triumph. You lose self and find love. Not automatically, but over time. Life makes sense in a way that doesn't make sense at all in the western perspective of existence. Time, possessions, wealth, none of it matters.

All you have left is faith. A faith that there is a deeper truth to this journey none of us asked to be sent upon. That God has a hand in our lives and that the Holy Spirit will console us and give us joy. Mother Teresa knew this. So did Ghandi, Mohammad, Buddha and a glorious legacy of saints and prophets through the past 30 centuries. There were others before them and before the written word was invented to take note of them. There will be more to follow.

So say this prayer with me. Try not to simply read it. Say it. Every line is both the riddle and the solution to the riddle. It is a wonderful prayer and, most importantly, it celebrates, as St. Francis did, our original innocence.

The Prayer Of St. Francis

Lord, make me an instrument of thy peace:
where there is hatred, let me sow love;
where there is injury, pardon;
where there is doubt, faith;
where there is despair, hope;
where there is darkness, light;
and where there is sadness, joy.
O Divine Master,
grant that I may not so much seek
to be consoled as to console;
to be understood as to understand;
to be loved, as to love;
for it is in giving that we receive,
it is in pardoning that we are pardoned,
and it is in dying that we are born to eternal life.

St Francis of Assissi
Italy, 13th Century

To Be Blessed By An Ocean

*L*ooking west, the gentle surf murmuring its timeless song, the sun tumbling back into the sea at the end of its long day's journey into night, I stand barefoot between the sea and the sand. Reflection comes easily here, the cold saltwater washing up just above my ankles and the sun momentarily balancing on the horizon like a gold coin standing on edge. So I let my thoughts wander where they may.

All I can think of is her. The contrasts between us are enormous. She is timeless, I am temporary. She is vast, expansive, unpredictable, elusive, blue and deep beyond measure. I am none of these things. She is the ocean - an azure canvas of wind and waves, of dappled sunlight and alluring mysteries. A canvas painted anew every morning by the hand of God. Fresh and vibrant, from a palate of sky blue and aquamarine.

How timeless is our relationship? Might not my feet be the feet of a native aboriginal a thousand, thousand years ago? A lonely human standing on this same distant beach, contemplating many of these same thoughts? Thoughts of my own mortality, of the beauty that is our brief existence, or the song of the sea? From the very dawn of self awareness, living in tribes along her shore, standing with our bare feet in the rolling waves, wondering why?

Wondering about our life. All important to us, yet insignificant in comparison to the grandeur of her awesome scale. Our eyes scan the endless plateau of the ocean for an answer. Gulls flock and dive off in the distance, working a school of minnows forced to the surface by a larger school of fish preying on them from below. Predators unseen by us.

Two bottlenose dolphins work their way down the beach. They pass so close to me that I can hear them throw open their blowholes to breathe as they swim. They breathe hard, searching for a wayward school of mullet to have for dinner.

I look down beneath my feet. Hundreds of tiny coquinas burrow back into the sand with each receding wave. The plovers, ibis and sandpipers scurry along this stretch of beach, ferreting out those coquinas that are not quite quick enough. To realize that this scene has not changed in a million years is to realize how timeless she is. How timeless life is.

But she does not respond to my questions. Nor will she ever answer them. The questions of man do not concern her. They belong to us alone. They belong to a world of rocks and metal, words and nations. She knows none of this. She has no boundaries, no clocks or compasses, no measures and no design. Like the universe itself, she defies our sad attempts at definition. To understand her at all, we will need to let go of this, this pride of syntax.

We need to let go of definition itself. We need to stand on this shoreline and not ask anything of it. Accepting all before us, and all within the depths beneath that endless surface, in a pause of perfect mindfulness. Only then will she allow us to enter her mystic silence. To not stand apart, but to look into her very soul, and in so doing, look into our soul. To see the tranquility as well as the hurricane, the mother of life and the hand of death. To know that in the end, they are the same. To acknowledge that the ocean is our earth's greatest blessing.

That from her everything has sprung forth. The primordial womb from which all life has evolved. That it is never a question of what she can give to us, but what we can give back to her. She fed us over the millennium and feeds us today as well. She gives us oxygen and moderates our climate, keeping the biosphere within that tiny range that allows us to exist.

We owe her everything. She gives us the wonder of rain. She gives us her rivers, like wandering children forever cascading back to their mother. We owe her our ships, our boats, our rafts and our kayaks. They were all designed and hewn by us to allow us to sail upon her endless seas, populating the distant continents and islands of this world. This homage could go on for volumes, but there is no need for it to do so. I have said enough.

The sun finally collapses into the sea as the moon rises in the east. Darkness gathers and the lights of the condominiums behind me light up one by one. Shellers appear in the distance, their flashlights cutting a feeble swath of light through the blackening sky. I put on my shoes and head back to my car to drive home. Nothing I can say matters to her as much as she matters to me. It is a love affair that will never end for me. I pray that somewhere in the depths of her heart, she feels the same.

Beyond Ice Fishing

*M*y family and I went up north for Christmas. Way, way north, where men wear insulated long underwear on all but the Fourth of July and don hats shaped like cheese bricks during the football season. Deer hunting territory, complete with bright orange outfits and Hamm's beer. Any further north and you run completely out of meaning.

During our stay in Duluth, a day or two after Christmas, a big news story broke. It happened somewhere in eastern Wisconsin. Apparently 17 grown men with severe testosterone poisoning, jumped the gun on ice fishing. After dragging their power augers and ice houses out upon a large frozen lake north of Milwaukee in search of famished perch, the ice-sheet they were fishing on broke off and floated out toward the center of the lake.

Lacking a boat, or any shred of common sense for that matter, several of them tried to swim back to the main body of ice. Three of them nearly drowned, and the rest were eventually lifted off the ice floe by a helicopter, having to abandon cases upon cases of beer and all their ice fishing equipment in the successful rescue.

The three who were trying to swim to safety likewise survived, but had body temperatures identical to a package of frozen peas when they were finally plucked out from the frigid waters. Luckily, their faculties were not developed enough to be affected by the incident. Next fall, they will proudly be wearing their cheese hats again, anxious to go ice fishing as soon as possible. Duhhh!

Which brings me to the question of ice fishing. Since my relatives know that I like to fish, several of them asked if I was planning to do any ice fishing while in Minnesota. "No," I replied tersely, in a manner that instantly curtailed any further discussion of the subject. They were serious, which is what really frightened me.

I did go ice fishing once. It was at my uncle's place on Fish Lake, just north of Duluth. My uncle Ray and his wife loved to ice fish. He invited me and my wife Molly to fish in his ice house. For those of you unfamiliar with ice houses, I can best describe them as small, outhouse sized buildings that sit out on a vast, flat plateau of cold, windswept ice. Anglers put them out as soon as the ice gets approximately six inches thick, if I remember correctly. They drag them either manually or by snowmobile. If the ice isn't quite ready, they fall through it and drown.

My uncle's ice house was, as ice houses go, an upscale model. He had a small wood stove in it. It boasted windows, coat hangers and little built-in drawers to store fishing tackle and Yukon Jack whiskey. It was the super deluxe model, insulated and the envy of all the other lunatics who ice fished on Fish Lake every winter.

The first thing you did upon entering this Hobbit-sized shelter was to start a fire in the wood stove. You did it to keep yourself from freezing to death. Starting a fire while sitting on six inches of ice has never struck me as sound thinking. After you get the ice house nice and warm, you take out the ice auger and proceed to drill a hole right through your floor. When you finally reach the lake water beneath the ice, it jets up through the floor for a minute until re-freezing again. If you are already jacked up on beer and whiskey, all of this is quite normal. If not, it is extremely disconcerting and cause for serious alarm.

Next, you take out these tiny little rods and lower a tiny chub minnow down through the six-inch hole you have made in the ice. Then you wait. And you wait. And you wait. You drink some more beer. And you wait. When you look up to talk to the person with you, you suddenly realize that his face isn't more than three inches from your face, so you try not to talk to him since your breath smells like booze. And you wait. You drink some more beer to help kill the pain. And you wait. Your feet eventually go numb. And you wait.

While you're waiting, you have to continually smash up this thin layer of ice that keeps reforming across your toilet-bowl-sized hole. They have designed handy little implements used for this that hang conveniently on the wall. On the one day in my life of ice fishing, neither Molly nor I had a bite. We lived through it, and I am thankful for that alone.

Just think of it. Seventeen adults, all standing there with ice augers and minnow buckets in hand, drifting out to sea on a break-away ice floe. Drifting out to meet their maker.

Before the invention of the helicopter, most of these men would have perished. Not that they wouldn't have captured an honorable mention in the Darwin Awards while doing so. But all this simply to catch malnourished walleyes on a frozen, desolate landscape. Even if you luck upon a good-sized northern pike or an errant muskie, it won't fit through the tiny little hole you've drilled.

So I have to ask you, dear reader, am I missing something here? Is ice fishing some form of self-mutilation that has become socially acceptable? Why not cut to the chase. Why not encourage self flagellation to all those Swedes and Norwegians who thrive up north? They could just stand there, barefoot in the snow and whip themselves with birch branches. Come to think of it, after taking their weekly saunas, they already do.

No, I'm beyond ice fishing. It's a "been there/done that" kind of experience at this point in my life. I'll leave that rare pleasure for others to enjoy. Dragging their ice house out across the icy wasteland, tempting fate. Listening to the ice crackle and crunch below their every step. Waiting to hear that final, thunderous crack just before your ski-doo falls through, heading for the mucky lake bottom twenty feet below.

Not that ice fishing is the only item on my "been there/done that" list. You can add to the list snowshoeing, winter camping and having to have my car jump-started in a howling blizzard. It's not that the South is perfect, because it isn't. It's just that you can't hot to death down here and the fishing, even at its worst, is a 1,000 times better than sitting in a small wooden cubicle on a tenuous sheet of ice trying to keep from freezing to death. And waiting. And waiting. And waiting.

To Hear The Sound Of Time

*I*t is just a dimestore clock. One of those folding travel clocks you find amidst the card decks and earplugs at your local drug store. Jet-black plastic, and powered by a single double "A" battery. I use it when our family hits the road on our long summer sojourns, or when I have to awake at 5:30 to head offshore to fish my favorite grouper holes or troll the Gulf Stream for the elusive dolphin. There is nothing extraordinary about it. It is just a travel alarm clock, round and costing less than five dollars.

Normally I keep the battery out of it, tucking it in the top left-hand drawer of my dresser amidst my laundered T-shirts. There, powerless and buried, it is as silent as starlight. When I take it out, I place the little battery lying beside it back in, set the time and double check the alarm setting. Then I place the clock beside my bed. That's when you can hear it: the sound of time.

Because it was built so inexpensively, probably in China or Malaysia, somewhere in the world where they are able to make things like this so affordable, it keeps time very loudly. A rusty sounding tick, tick, tick marks off every sixty seconds like those NFL refs mark off the forward progress of a winning football team. In the dead of night, the ticking becomes even louder, as though the refs were asked to bring out the chains every single play to double-check. Noisy chains at that, amidst a stadium full of even louder fans.

It used to annoy me. Like a dripping faucet or a branch hitting the side of your house in a gusty wind, the steady tick, tick, tick would keep me awake half the night. Sometimes I would place it back in my dresser still ticking, knowing that the alarm would cut through the muffling nature of the T-shirts but that the rusty ticking noise would not. The half dozen times I used this method, it worked.

Then, about a month ago, I changed. For reasons unexplainable, the ticking no longer bothered me. It soothed and calmed me, like the rhythmic hum of an electric fan, or the sound of the wind in the pines. It was no longer a relentless, rusty tick after tick after tick. It was only the sound of time.

Time that told me that all is finite. Me, you, the world itself. Every sixty clicks just a minute of eternity that is, was, and will never again be. Unique, yet oddly the same. The elusive nature of the eternal present.

Maybe it's just that I'm going to be 50 this year. They keep sending me junk mail from AARP and I keep writing "return to sender," on it, hoping that they will take me off of their computerized mailing list. The thought of turning 50 seems so strange to me, so final. But then again so did 40. Now that I'm thinking about it, 30 was equally difficult.

But time is such an elusive mistress, such a vain enigma. Sometimes I used to think of my life as though I was nothing more than a drop of water on a red hot skillet. The instant that water hits the cast iron frying pan, it dances wildly about for an instant and then vanishes into steam. In the grand scheme of life, in a way, that is all we really are. Beads of water dancing on the jagged surface of a lonely planet circling a single sun on the edge of some enormous galaxy. Each of us lasting little more than the length of each tick of my dimestore clock.

Thank goodness I finally let that one go. Now I watch my boys grow as tall as the royal palms we planted a decade ago and I see each sunrise with a clarity I thought that I would never know. I cherish each and every tick of that dimestore clock, thanking God for letting me be here to appreciate the sound of time.

It's like what Doc said to me a few weeks ago when we were running around the indigo blue waters off of Marathon looking for schools of dolphin that were nowhere to be found. I said to him that we weren't having much luck today and started to apologize for a lousy day of fishing. Doc looked at me and laughed, having trumped me with his 78 years of wisdom in one terse reply, "We're lucky just to be here."

Indeed, Doc, we are. Every tick, tick, tick of it. Lucky to experience the joys, the sorrows and the journey. Once understood and accepted, the glass is always half full, and the water in it tastes as sweet as the air we breathe. Glorious. We're lucky just to be here. Indeed, we are.

In Digger's Memory

*I*killed a gopher tortoise. It was an accident. It was back in September, 1999, on the morning of my boys' joint birthday party. I was in a terrible hurry, trying to make the house ready for a mob of 15 nine- and ten-year-old boys. I wasn't paying much attention to my driving.

I had taken my Landcruiser over to Bailey's grocery store to pick up a half-dozen bags of ice for the party that afternoon. When I pulled back into my yard I wanted to leave the driveway open for the soon-to-be-arriving parents, so I cut the corner sharper than usual and drove up and over the lawn instead of keeping on the driveway.

He must have been down there, grazing on the freshly-cut grass. Because the bougainvilleas are so tall, and I cut behind them so sharply, there was no way for me to see the tortoise. As my back tire ran over him I made a mental note of the unexpected bump. I thought that one of the boys had left a coconut or something lying in the yard. That's how boys are, careless at times.

When I got out of the truck, ice bags in hand, I looked back to see what it was I had run over. My heart stopped when I saw that it wasn't a coconut or a misplaced toy, but a turtle. Worse than that, it was our turtle. Logan, my oldest boy, had appropriately named him "Digger" five years before.

I dropped the ice on the driveway and ran back to see how he was doing. As I stood over him, I knew instantly that he was killed. The weight of the 6,000-pound truck had just caught the back half of his body, but the damage it had done was overwhelming. His shell had simply exploded and his organs and stomach were lying next to him in a tangled mess. This was not a trauma that a tortoise can survive. Both of his hind legs were crushed and there was blood everywhere. I knew at once that the careful hands over at CROW couldn't save an animal this broken.

As I stood there, tears welling up in my eyes, I noticed that Digger was still alive. As an instinctive reaction to the impact of the tire upon him, he had pulled his head and front legs back into his shell. He looked up at me as though to try to tell me something, but I didn't understand what his dark eyes were saying.

I couldn't let the boys see what had just happened. I ran back and got a shovel and scooped Digger's shattered body unto it. I walked across the street and set him down amidst the tall weeds and grasses and left him there. Left him there to die. I then ran up and took out our garden hose, being careful to rinse the dark red blood off the grass and wash away the many pieces of broken shell that lay scattered around the yard where he was hit.

Unexpectedly, Logan yelled out to me from the front porch, "What are you doing, Dad?"

I didn't know what to say. His birthday party was starting in less than an hour and he didn't need to see Digger this way. It would have cast such a terrible shadow on such a wonderful event. I lied.

"Oh, I'm just hosing the grass I mowed yesterday off of the bricks here. It looks so messy and all."

"OK, Dad, but Mom needs the ice up here as soon as you're done."

"Will do, Logan. Will do."

As he headed back into the house I glanced back over to where Digger was dying. The image of his face, his rough dark skin and jet-black eyes, withdrawn into his shell in some useless effort of self defense, was forever burned into my memory. I blamed myself and I still do. I should have pulled up slower, I should have used the driveway, I should have walked to Baileys, I should have...what difference does it make? Accidents happen.

But I keep thinking about that gopher tortoise. Seeing that frightened look on his face, seeing him mortally wounded beneath the wheel of my careless SUV, Digger is impossible to forget. I realize that Digger had tried to protect himself from my Landcruiser using the same mechanisms of self-defense he had used for the last million years. Whether it was a curious bobcat looking for a dinner or a ten-foot alligator chewing on his rock hard shell, the gopher tortoise uses the same tried and true technique to save itself: pull your legs and head in and wait it out.

Were that only true for wildlife in the world today. Could the porcupine simply put up his quills and stop the deforestation of the old growth forests, or the mighty Jaguar roar away the bulldozers and construction cranes that are invading the tropical rain forests. Then these wild creatures would have little to fear. But they cannot.

They have no defense against us. No voice. No chance to survive save that which we grant them.

For what happened to Digger in my driveway that September is what is happening to thousands of species across the globe, from San-Cap Road to India. Pulling their legs and head inside of their shells will not save them from the sheer tonnage of mankind's march of progress. The weight is too much for their shells to take. What has worked for wildlife for the last billion years of evolution means nothing to a globe crawling with SUVs, sprawling development and endless consumerism. Something has to give.

It is the shell of the tortoise that gives. Habitat shrinks, wild places vanish beneath a flood of asphalt and the world loses, one species at a time. We lose right along with it. Our children, and the generations beyond lose even more.

Can we change? Live with less and find that we have all the more for it? Give back to the earth what she has so graciously given us? Volunteer at places like Ding Darling, or give to SCCF or CROW. Become a voice for the creatures that cannot speak. Do what we can, when we can, however we can; advocate, recycle, donate. Anything that can help. Anything that would make the next thousand years of human history something to be proud of.

Maybe that's what Digger was trying to tell me when he looked up at me with his dark eyes and dying breath. If so, I hope I heard him.

*Footnote: I have since learned that CROW (which stands for the Clinic for the Rehabilitation of Wildlife) here on Sanibel has a euthanasia program for mortally wounded animals. In hindsight, I know that I should have taken Digger in to be put to sleep. I pray that I never have to do either of these things in my lifetime again.

In an effort to make amends, I dedicated my second novel, *Way Under Contract* to Digger and donated one dollar of every sale of the book to conservation purposes. A portion of those monies goes to helping to save sea turtles, Digger's next of kin.

The Guests Are Gone

*E*aster came early this year and I was glad. It felt like the bell going off in the eleventh round of a fight that I was losing, and losing badly. My vision was blurred, my nose broken in two places and I was staggering helplessly. All I could think of as I hit the mat was that they were flying out the weekend after Easter Sunday. It was over. The referee was calling the fight. Our last batch of house guests were finally leaving.

And now the guests are gone. Gone as well is our last gallon of milk, all my Ben & Jerry's ice cream, the laundry detergent, all of my Mount Gay rum, a case and a half of Heineken and my wife's secret stash of chocolates. Gone is my patience. Gone is my sense of humor.

They have taken it all, those old friends and shoestring relatives who thrive on their annual southern invasion each and every winter. You all know whom I'm talking about. Your brother and his overweight wife from Peoria; that nephew you never really liked and his two punk college friends, that roommate of yours from Penn State or, in a worst case scenario, your mother-in-law and her new boyfriend.

Her new boyfriend who has the personality of a snail. A snail that chain smokes cheap cigars and, although he would deny it until the bitter end, prefers to smoke them in the guest bathroom with the fan on. As if it helps.

They have all headed back up north again. Leaving your house a mess, your electric and water bills at record levels and your faith in humanity in serious question. You can barely remember that wonderful conversation you had with Uncle Clem last October when he just happened to mention that he and Aunt Martha might be coming down next February and they were wondering if they might be able to spend a few nights at your place.

They stayed two-and-a-half weeks. Uncle Clem immediately commandeered your remote and you were forced to watch hours of all-star wrestling matches in lieu of Ken Burns' new documentary on PBS. After awhile it hardly mattered. They broke both of your bicycles the first week of their protracted stay and would stroll into the kitchen asking, "What's cookin'?" religiously every evening around six-thirty. You looked over at the both of them, bored of watching body slams and slugging down your last few Heineken, as thoughts of cannibalism ran through your mind. "What's cookin'?" you pondered. Uncle Clem and Aunt Martha. Stewed.

But there was no reprieve. After they drove back to Dayton the next batch were already registering in the driveway. Pulling up with their rusty minivan, hungry and ready to head to the beach. This time they came unannounced. It was your third cousin Andy and his expectant wife along with their two incorrigible kids. They were from Nebraska. You had met them once before, nine years ago at a family picnic in Wichita. They were virtual strangers. They could have randomly picked a name out of the Sanibel phone directory and been as closely related. Shoestring relatives would be a kind description. Thread-bare in-laws might work, a second cousin through a failed marriage on your distant uncle's side of the family. Strangers with an hearty appetite.

And the wife, having contractions in the kitchen while her two kids are in the guest bedroom using x-acto knives on the wallpaper. Spoiled brats who don't like to eat fish, or shrimp or ethnic foods of any kind. Kids whose diet consists of Lucky Charms, pizza and plain spaghetti. Two boys, an eight-year-old and a ten-year-old who whine constantly and swell up with hundreds of tiny bug bites if they go outside for more than 60 seconds. Children so ghostly white that only sunblock with an SPF factor of 100 or better could prevent them from burning. After the first few days they didn't need to go to the beach. They had tracked in so much sand that they could build their enormous sandcastles in the family room.

House guests. A Florida tradition that dates back to the Calusa.

I can hear them now, "Honey, are these Apaches ever going to leave?" The phone calls start in September and the deluge stops only after you've decided to move back north or the bell rings on Easter Sunday. All that's left behind is their sad collection of broken shells they forgot on your back porch, the stain on your new Berber carpet where their toy poodle threw up and those guilty feelings you have about cannibalism.

Excuse me, I have to get the phone. It's my sister and her family calling from Minnesota. You've guessed it, they're coming down next week. I think I'll move to Toledo.

Someplace Called Orlando

*W*e stood in front of the walrus tank for the longest time, watching the three of them interact in an eerie silence. There was an element of surrealism to the tableau that morning at Sea World; the strange fluorescent blue lights beneath the dome, the thick, curving plexiglass, the imitation icebergs in the background.

My wife and I knew how strange it really was, standing just a few feet from three blubbery walruses on a clear, crisp January morning in central Florida. Strange and intriguing. The male must have weighed over 3,000 pounds, his long ivory tusks quite useless in this brave new world of Orlando.

Maybe it's just me. There is something about that town that promises far more than it ever delivers. Killer whales that gently kiss their trainers. Fake streets with fake stores that sell replicas of things far removed from their native lands. An entire city built on the premise that pretending to be what you are not is normal. Now they even have a fake Key West, albeit lacking in authentic derelicts who still inhabit the real Duval Street.

But it's not just me. My wife feels it as well, although her symptoms aren't as acute. Within 24 hours of arrival I generally break out in a severe case of post-modern alienation. You know, the whole *Catcher in the Rye* Holden Caufield thing. The overwhelming urge to hug a tree. A real tree.

The trouble being is that Orlando doesn't stop at the theme parks any longer. It's like some kind of imitation virus that's infecting the entire town. International Drive looks more and more like something out of a *Star Wars* set. The hotels and resorts keep getting stranger and stranger and everywhere you turn there's another attraction: King Henry's Feast, The World of China, Medieval Times, the list is endless.

And none of it is real. Sixty years ago it was a small farm town with a railroad, some marginal orange groves and a fair share of cattle. Now it's mankind's crowning centerpiece of deception. At Epcot you can stroll from England to Mexico to Africa in a half an hour. Everything sanitized, safe and made out of plaster of Paris.

It is a shame that millions of foreign visitors come to Orlando each and every year to find out what America is like. If America were anything like Orlando, I would move to New Zealand in a heartbeat. When I think of America I like to picture the royal blue grain elevators of southern Ohio, the Golden Gate Bridge spanning San Francisco Bay and the arid plains of Texas. Those are real things, real places with real people working the land, crossing the great bridge out to Sausalito or driving for hours across an open range. None of these Americas are designed by computer geeks and made from extruded plastic.

But Orlando is a part of America. A troublesome part. It's a place of dreams: of twisting roller coasters, King Kong and Mickey Mouse. It started out humbly enough with Disney World. A fantasy come true. Now I'm afraid it's hemorrhaging. It's a town out of control with its own hyperactive imagination. Every new roller coaster is longer, steeper, more thrilling than the last one. Every animal show is more spectacular, more amazing, more unreal. Less and less like the way wild animals would behave.

Friends of mine will sometimes spend a week up there. Why? I get disoriented after two days. I start to question whether the stone crabs I've just ordered are really stone crabs or just some kind of Orlando food made out of hydrogenated jellies and poly-carbonated resins. Not to mention what the hamburgers and French fries are extracted from.

My biggest fear is that this Orlando disease will keep spreading. That it will overtake every village and town in this beautiful country of ours. That Ding Darling will soon be adding a section of electronic roseate spoonbills in lieu of having to deal with the whims of the real ones. You know, the spoonbills that don't always show up on time.

That everything, everywhere will be a replica of what it once was. That charm will be fabricated, character mass-produced and integrity just a matter of coming up to the ticket booth with enough of a VISA credit line to get you through the door.

Stuck in this huge amusement park without hope for parole. I know that Orlando is sacred to some of you who are reading this column. My boys still love it, as all children do. It's just me. I have this thing about a world too perfect and a healthy aversion to idols. Maybe I'm just needlessly looking over my shoulder for an approaching Moses. Well, when you think about it, that's not so bad either.

The Ghosts Of Christmases Past

*T*he cold air sweeps down from Canada and across the hills of northern Minnesota, rushing toward the southern sun like a child wanting for the warmth of its mother, cold air that was held captive in the endless night high above the Arctic Circle. The temperature drops relentlessly as the child of winter races south. Fifteen above falls quickly to zero. Zero slips by and the air outside is a menacing ten below.

Everything is frozen. Automobile tires make a distinctive crunching sound as they carefully navigate through the hard-packed snow and ice. At first the lakes freeze; soon thereafter the rivers and creeks become too cold to flow. The snow drifts across the open spaces, forming pure white waves that never break. The sun hesitates on the horizon, ashamed to raise its head above this lifeless scene. It shines from habit, its warmth but a memory of mid-October.

Winter is everywhere upon my hometown, Duluth, Minnesota. From the chimneys that ride above the Christmas decorations and the white, white landscape surrounding those decorated homes, ghosts pour forth. Steam and smoke rise briefly above the rooftops and vanish in the stiff arctic breeze. Inside the drafty homes, families reunite. They gather amidst colorful wrappings and lavish dinners to smile and pose for pictures that end up in photo albums. Albums that will fade over time, showing candid shots of great aunts and children who have grown old and married. Photo albums that lose importance with every passing decade.

As much as Christmas is a celebration of the living family, it is, in an unspoken ritual, a remembrance of families past. It is a time of ghosts. A time when we remember more than the quick. Conversations tend to linger over friends who have passed on, family members who have divorced or are no longer here to enjoy these moments with us. Remembrances of Christmases past and Christmases yet to come.

"Did you hear that Dean Johnson died of a massive heart attack last summer? You remember him, Charlie, don't you? He never did get married. Smoked more than he should have, that's for sure. Graduated the same year I did. Can you imagine that?"

"They finally split up, must be six, seven years ago now. Shelly just got fed up with his drinking and filed for divorce. I don't know what happened to their oldest boy, Bruce. Last I heard, he was out in Wyoming working for some oil company. Their youngest, Jimmy, is still in town. Harry quit drinking and remarried. I saw him about two years ago down at the Apple Festival. He looks good for his age."

"When they opened her up, they found that the cancer was just about everywhere. The doctor just shook his head and sewed her back together. Martha died about a month later. It was for the better in the end. She was in such pain and all."

Long conversations over eggnog and rum-ball cookies. Eulogies over loved ones long since lost to the hands of fate and time. Names, places and events abandoned in the winding corridors of our memories. This is no coincidence, this strange unspoken ritual.

Four days before the celebration of Christmas we pass through the portal of the winter solstice. The darkest and shortest day of the year. The sun up north barely slips above the horizon and in a matter of hours, the fleeting daylight is gone. It is the passing of another year and our hearts feel it, even if our minds do not. It is a ritual of passage, as ancient as winter.

As we page through those old photo albums, we secretly know that these flash bulbs now lighting up the dining room will likewise capture us. We will then become the ghosts of Christmases yet to come, when our children will look at aging picture albums and remember back to this same dated décor, the same faded smiles. The sad lament of change, like the air outside, rushing south. I leave you only with this question. What prayer, save love, can make sweet sense of life?

Three Feet From Death

*B*ad novels have a way of sticking with you, even when they are your own. Back in the late 1970s, I stumbled across an idea for a novel that, like a persistent, hacking cough, I've never been able to shake. God help me, I've tried.

The name of the novel is the same as the name of this column: *Three Feet From Death*. It was a murder mystery with more than its fair share of Zen. The story began in India, probably because I was on a Rudyard Kipling kick at the time. It had that classic, "It was a dark, humid night on the outskirts of Bombay when..." feel to it. That pulp fiction feel.

But the novel ran out of steam on page three. Nothing could save it: not the menacing Bengal tiger, not the black cobra, not even the thuggee assassins could keep the storyline from suffering full cardiac arrest. The novel ended up in the circular file, taking its place beside a couple of empty cans of diet Mountain Dew and a stale quarter-bag of cheese popcorn. Novelist nourishment at its finest.

That was my one and only stab, so to speak, at murder mysteries. I've always found them so preposterous and out of sync with the world we live in. When people do get murdered down here on planet earth (which happens daily, by the way, and is accordingly documented by the evening news) it's usually by a relative or a spouse with a bad attitude. Add a half-dozen gunshots which the neighbors say, and I quote them here, "It sounded like fireworks," and there you have it: murder one. Just an alienated victim taking a handful of rounds to the torso and another roll of bright yellow police tape surrounding the empty house.

Some mystery.

No, it was the Zen that intrigued me more than the "Whodunnit?" aspect of my horrific attempt at writing my first novel. The premise of the book was that my lead character, a ruddy Englishman with a penchant for trouble, was never further than three feet from death. Be it one wrong step on the snow-capped Himalayas, a rhino charge in northern India, or a plane crash near Malaysia, my ill-fated protagonist was never more than a few baby steps from his own mortality.

Granted, the premise was bad and the action overwrought. It was like a Sylvester Stallone movie on steroids. The commotion was non-stop, the scenes more contrived than a shootout at an Orlando theme park, and the characters as thin and transparent as Glad wrap. Nobody in his right mind would have bought into the manic action in *Three Feet From Death*. Luckily, no one will ever have to.

Which brings me to the theme of this essay. The theme being that, in fact, all of us live a mere three feet from death. Not in the bad novel sense of the term, but in a bad sense of reality. Be it an unexpected stroke, arrhythmia, a car accident, a bad fall, or a disgruntled fellow worker, we are all subject to the whims of our own unknown fate. The happenstance of our own unanticipated demise.   Not that anyone reading this will probably have an Australian pine fall on them this afternoon, or be bitten by a coral snake lying in wait beside the broken sprinkler head. It's not something we can even spare a minute to think about, caught up as all of us are with the pleasures of life and not the apprehension of its terminal nature. And well we should be caught up in this wondrous web of existence.

But our life is a fragile web, strung between young saplings in a windstorm, and we should never lose sight of that. By appreciating the tenuous nature of your own existence, you cherish the minute. You remember to kiss your wife, or your husband in the morning and you take the time to smell the gardenias along the way, thinking in a distant part of your heart that this might be the last time you may ever inhale their sweet, captivating fragrance. Life becomes more intense, more vital and far more important.

Because there is an inevitability to the fact that someday, past midnight in the dark of the stars, that telephone ringing will be the news of your death delivered by a saddened friend to someone who would want to know. That someday might be tomorrow, and it might be 30 years from now. But that phone will ring as sure as the earth will go on spinning.

So try to think of yourself as the lead character in a bad novel if it helps. Keep an eye out for crouching tigers, Firestone tires, malfunctioning regulators, rogue waves, drunken drivers, defective stepladders and your cholesterol level. Not that it will ultimately keep you out of the hands of the grim reaper, because it won't. It's just that it will make you that much more aware of the splendor that is your next breath. Now get out of here and go catch a sunset, provided a micro-meteor doesn't get to you first.

Come to think of it, maybe I should take a second look at writing murder mysteries? Look for it in the fall, *Three Feet From Death, a Sanibel Story.*

No, it's already been done. I'll stick to Zen.

In The Mangroves

*T*he 14-foot Jon-boat skims right along, just fast enough to keep us up on plane. As evening gathers, Jim and I are winding our way through this labyrinth of roots and trees that makes up this red mangrove forest.

We slow down now and again to drift idly through the narrow cuts that eventually lead out to the bay. For it is here where the fish like to lie, pointing their long, lissome bodies into the current. Waiting to prey on whatever rides down these curious tidal rivers that flow both ways.

As if synchronized with the falling sunset, the tide is likewise falling. It is always then, just after the turn of the tide, in the first few hours of the ebb tide, that the large fish come out to feed.

Jim and I are both quiet now, concentrating on every cast. We are both trying hard to land our lures on the very edge of the gnarled and twisted red mangrove roots. Many casts fall short.

But we are also quiet for other, more compelling reasons. There is nothing here to say that could be said as perfectly as witnessing a young osprey gracefully collapse before its dive on a huge school of mullet a hundred yards to the north of us. Nothing that we could say would belong above the squabble of a small flock of white ibis strutting 50 feet back in this strange, subtropical forest.

In our tacit silence we can hear the loud "Pohhhh," of two large bottlenose dolphins working their way down the tidal creek. They are hunting for the same fish we are: the bronze-colored redfish, the elusive snook, and the colorful sea trout. The difference being that their search is in earnest. Perhaps because of this overwhelming sense of alive, little is ever said. Just the quiet of cast after cast.

Our gold and silver spoons making their small splashes near the deeply undercut banks. Their momentum carrying them forward even under the water, sliding down well under an overhanging bush. High above the limb roosts an awkward anhinga, its wings opened wide, drying in the fading sunlight. Its long snakelike neck silhouetted against an ever-darkening sky. Beside us drifts a solitary blue crab, looking lost in this current, mistaking our boat for a raft of uprooted turtle grass. The clump of grass is floating calmly back out to sea. As are we.

Just then the silence is shattered by the impact of a pale golden snook smashing Jim's lure. The fish's massive head quickly comes out of the water, shaking furiously from side to side, trying like all hell to throw the treble hook. The lure is firmly lodged in the shaking fish's mouth. The peace is dashed with exclamations like, "He's got to be better than 20 pounds!" or, "Keep him away from the mangrove roots, or he'll cut you off!"

But even as my warning is sounded, he makes a determined dash to the edge of the creek, headstrong and fighting to survive. Jim's line barely touches the barnacle encrusted roots and all is lost.

Jim reels in the frayed and parted line and mumbles something about losing such a trophy. Losing another battle to the mangrove roots that encircle this estuary. But his complaint is soon drowned out by the loud squawking of a nearby great blue heron who is displeased with our presence in his territory.

And so this game of angling is played from creek to creek with a pious conviction. Some evenings the fish are stacked up in *Jewfish Creek*, and on other afternoons they all seem to be in *Duffy's Creek*. Then there are days when the fish are nowhere to be found.

But it doesn't matter. Most of the time we release them anyway. In this regard we differ dramatically from the two large porpoises that passed us an hour ago. Theirs is an imperative. Ours is an aesthetic. Ours is listening to the eternal rhythms of a sea that flows both ways.

Ours is the sound of a cracking shrimp beneath the thin aluminum skin of this jon-boat. The brief sighting of a trio of manatees making their way back out toward the bay with this ebb tide. The three of them making certain that they will not be caught back here at dead low tide, when the water will be all but gone.

Ours is the vision of a 12-pound redfish tugging on the other end of that thin thread of monofilament as the sun vanishes into the Gulf of Mexico. It is a battle that you cannot lose. If you do not catch a thing, you still have this very moment to be forever etched in your heart. This moment in this sanctuary of life. If you do catch a fish, you can set it free again, hoping that someday you will meet again.

And so it is that the afternoon wanes to sunset and the sunset wanes to nightfall. Soon, finding the edge of these bushy mangroves becomes too challenging for our casting skills. Finally, when all the details are lost to this darkness all-descending, I pull the hand cord to my little 9.9 h.p. Yamaha and head toward home.

So much water has poured out of this patch of mangroves that I have to be careful to stick to only the deepest channels. The shallow grass flats lie exposed, covered with roseate spoonbills and great white egrets looking for a last errant baitfish or two before flying off to roost for the night.

By midnight the tide will change again, flowing back in across these mud flats and sandbars in an even deeper silence. This ritual of life will go on as it has for a million years. The long, slender bodies of the fishes will reverse direction and the salt water will rush back in on the flood tide. It is as if the earth is breathing, this water flowing in and out, in and out in the mangroves.

Breathing the beautiful breath of eternity.

The Trost Parcel

*W*e had discovered it by accident. Steven, my younger brother, and I had been walleye fishing along the southern shore of St. Louis Bay in my 17-foot canoe. St. Louis Bay lies between Minnesota and Wisconsin at the very western tip of Lake Superior. The walleyes had come back into the bay after the steel mill on the Duluth side of the bay had closed.

As we trolled along the edge of steep clay bluffs with the small electric motor, we found it. It was a great blue heron rookery. Had it not been for the tremendous squawking the herons made as we drew near their nesting site, I doubt that we would have noticed it. High amongst a stand of mixed Norway and white pine the birds had built their nests. There were over 50 nests in all.

Steven and I pulled up to the shoreline just below the heart of the rookery and climbed out of the canoe to investigate. We tied the canoe off to an alder bush and climbed up the steep, muddy bank. The herons were going wild high above us. To them, we suddenly became a mother's worst nightmare. In their eyes, we were predators.

As hundreds of herons screamed in panic high above us, we walked to the top of the 20-foot ridge and looked up in awe. The nests were 40 to 50 feet above us, wedged in carefully between the strong, symmetrical branches of the pines. Many of the nests had chicks in them. At our feet were years of bird droppings, feathers and an occasional skeleton. Small skeletons, probably of chicks who had fallen out of the nests in years past. But what I remember most about that moment some 20 years ago, was the tremendous din.

The large birds awkwardly flew from branch to branch, looking down at us nervously. There were nearly 100 herons in all, and every bird was squawking at us as loudly as possible. The noise was maddening. Steven and I both said that we should come back with a camera someday and quickly hurried back down to our canoe. We had to shout to each other as we spoke, it was so deafening.

We never went back with the camera. As we slipped away, the birds settled back down and the silence of the bay slowly replaced the clamor. Steven and I realized that we should never have stepped out of that canoe. By doing so, we had unknowingly violated an unwritten code of nature. We had trespassed into their home. A home of some 70 tall pines on the edge of a deserted finger of the southern shore of St. Louis Bay. If we were to come across a single bird, feeding along a shoreline somewhere, no doubt it would simply fly off and find another place to dine.

But a rookery is different. The chicks cannot fly off. The mothers become alarmed and panic. I was later to learn that at times like these, in the midst of all the commotion, chicks will often become over-excited and accidently fall. If the rookery is disturbed once too often, the entire site will be abandoned.

These birds don't ask for much. Less than an acre. But that acre has to be private, and that acre has to be respected, lest we incur their wrath. All living creatures need a place to call home.

This is why losing the Trost parcel to development is unacceptable. I spoke with Eric Lindblad from the Sanibel-Captiva Conservation Foundation about the property. There isn't one rookery on this 165-acre tract. There are *five!* Along this quiet, untrodden stretch of the Sanibel River nest little blue herons, anhingas, yellow-crowned night herons, tri-colored herons and little green herons. There are hundreds upon hundreds of nests.

Up along the largest remaining tract of a mid-island ridge roam more gopher tortoises than anywhere else on the island. Most of these ridges have long since fallen to development, to shopping centers, golf courses and the uprootings of man. The ridge remains untouched on the Trost parcel. An ancient stretch of piled up beach, riddled with gopher tortoise burrows.

The Trost parcel represents nearly two percent of the entire island of Sanibel. It runs along the east side of Tarpon Bay Road from West Gulf Drive to the southern edge of Bailey's General Store. It is currently owned by Herta Trost from Frankfurt, Germany, and is the last major piece of open land left on Sanibel. To save it will take nearly three million dollars. To lose it is not an option.

Every day, all of us who choose to live on this Sanctuary Island, or those of us who simply come to visit, do so because we love its commitment to nature. We all enjoy the miles of bike path, winding through acres of unspoiled spartina grasses and sabal palms. To us, they are Sanibel.

All those herons, turtles and wild things ask in return is for us to give them some room. Some private, untouched spaces so they can build their modest homes here as well. Homes of sticks and mud. Places where they can raise the next generation of those birds whose photographs adorn our condominiums, homes and restaurants. Places where the wild things roam.

The Conservation Foundation has until next May to raise the money. Someone reading this column can help, or knows someone who can. Three million dollars is one hell of a lot of money. Eric Lindblad, the director of SCCF knows this, as do all of the wonderful people at the Foundation. Nothing worthwhile comes cheaply or easily.

Look at it another way. The Trost parcel has already been developed by the herons, ospreys and gopher tortoises. It has achieved its "highest and best use." Nothing short of clearing out the exotics and protecting it forever can be done to improve this beautiful property. So for now, the best thing for us to do is to slip quietly back into our canoes and let it be.

*footnote: The money to purchase the Trost parcel was raised, in thanks to a one million dollar contribution from a family who dedicated the money in honor of their mother, Frannie. It is now known as Frannie's Preserve. The pepper and most of the Australian pines have been cut down and burned off. The rookeries have remained untouched.

Hopefully, they will remain untouched forever.

Falling Down

*D*o you remember the last time you watched an infant taking his first few steps? Can you still picture the wobbly legs, the lack of balance and the joy that child expressed when he finally succeeded? At times it isn't so much an exercise in walking as it is in falling down.

The child doesn't mind. After every tumble, he carefully stands back up and begins his tentative journey once again. The youngster is determined to walk and falling down is just a part of the cost of learning something new. The price he has to pay for changing. The toddler is afraid, but he never lets his fear overtake his sense of determination. Too young to feel foolish or ashamed, the child accepts his tumbles with a steadfast smile.

As we grow older, we grow taller. Taller both physically and emotionally. We become reluctant to change, even when we realize that changing will make it easier to get where we would like to be. We resist changing or taking any uncertain risks. Perhaps we have grown too tall for our own good. We have become afraid of falling down.

Part of it is fear and part of it is pride, this anxiety we have about falling down. I've given a lot of thought to this: how we arrive at being who we are, and how we might discover who else we might be.

Most of us simply don't go there. Most of us confine ourselves and our lives within well-kept fences of our own design. Pleasant fences, complete with fine white pickets and delicate scroll work, but fences nonetheless.

We abandon some of our talents along the way, or forgo friends and relationships which we decide are too difficult to pursue. We sell ourselves short, keeping our lives held safely within these well-tended enclosures of our own decisions.

That childlike perseverance that once kept our knees bruised and our dreams alive is slowly, methodically abandoned. We become our own habit, our own well-studied ritual of time and place, family and friends that all fit into our comfortable self-image. Here, inside this safe and calculated place, we pass the time of life allowed to us in what Emerson described as our "quiet desperation."

But what do we sacrifice along the way? What about that journey, that voyage that you promised yourself but never broke out of your ritual long enough to take? By keeping within the narrow parameters of these self-imposed landscapes we leave so many of our dreams behind. The unpainted canvases, the unwritten manuscripts and the silence of those piano lessons you have always managed to avoid taking.

Fear of falling down, and the hurt pride that comes with having to fall, having to fail, keeps you from even trying. Having to throw those first few mediocre paintings away, embarrassed by your lack of talent. Having to break out of those familiar, well-rehearsed patterns to take the time to sit down and enjoy a sunset or awake an hour earlier to catch a glorious daybreak. Receiving your first D in decades because you elected to take that course you have been putting off for years at the local college.

In the end it isn't just pride, it's vanity. We become so self-conscious, so afraid of failing that we keep to crawling along with the way things are instead of daring to do the unexpected. We never call that old friend of ours because...well, we just don't. We never apologize for hurting someone five years ago because we just can't find the time. That's not true. We just don't make the time.

We live inside our well-manicured yard, safe with the knowledge of who we are and free of the bruised knees and hurt egos that come with leaving our usual scripts. Sadly, it is the way of life for most of us.

But look again the next time you see that toddler taking those first tentative steps. Look beyond the tumbles and the tears and see the sheer joy in that child's eyes. Watch him as he gathers confidence and grows. Watch him quickly learn not just to walk, but to run. Run toward his glorious future.

Falling down...we should all try it sometime. The tears will quickly vanish, the bruises heal and the dream will prove to be more than worth the effort.

To Catch a Catfish
(1994-1998)

The Rhythm Of The Tides

*T*he tides are the heartbeat of the sea. The surging water of the flood tide and the slow retreat of the ebb tide are rhythms that have gone unbroken for a billion years. Expansive tidal flats vanish beneath the sea as planets, moons and suns align and un-align. Six hours later those same flats lie vulnerable and exposed. In and out, in and out, this cosmic heartbeat goes on. We take the tides for granted and we plan our journeys, moor our boats and, should we fish, study the tide charts in an attempt to pick the perfect tides to fish upon.

But like everything in nature, the tides cannot be relied upon. A strong wind can blow far more water out of the bay than your chart had indicated. A hurricane can force the high tide to rise above the docks, and stretch the limits of our carefully tethered lines. The tide charts are in error. The scientists who labored so intensely over them could not have known about the wind, or the run off from the heavy storm, the unforeseen surge of a hurricane, the unpredictable changes that would unravel their careful calculations.

How could those learned men have known that the tropical depression to the south would siphon out all the water from the bay, leaving it impossible to navigate in all but the deepest of channels? Things happen, and the ebb and flow of the rhythm becomes disrupted. Broken.

In late October of 1996 my life was likewise disrupted. The natural cadence, the rhythm of living was shattered by an unexpected phone call in the late afternoon of October 23rd from my oldest sister

Barbara. Like a storm to the south, in tears, she relayed the tragic news that my little sister Peggy had been killed in a car accident on Interstate 35 outside Duluth. The rhythm of the tides was lost. Everything poured out of me at once, leaving only an emptiness defined by immense loss.

My little sister Peggy was a saint. By that I don't mean that she was angelic, or that she didn't have her own set of demons to deal with. She drank a mean white Russian and she was always eager to dance 'til dawn. Peg had a passion for enjoying life and over the forty years she spent down here, she managed to do more; laugh more, cry more and love more than most people fit into their allotted seventy.

She was a human saint. If you had a problem that you couldn't handle, the rule was to call Peg. There were nearly 500 people at the funeral that cold and clear afternoon in Duluth and all of them were there for her because Peg was always there for them. Some had last seen her when they were 12 years-old together up at the lake. One girl had met Peg two weeks before when she offered to pierce her ears for free at a party they were both attending. Half drunk, at midnight with an ear piercing kit Peg kept in her purse and a smile on Peg's face, this newfound friend had pierced ears. That was my little sister Peg.

For over fifteen years she was an LPN at St. Luke's Hospital. Peg worked on the geriatric ward and over her years there had comforted hundreds of elderly men and women as they passed away in the night. She had held the hand of my Grandmother, Clara, the afternoon she died. My grandmother died at 95. In the end, Clara lived 55 years longer than did Peg.

Life had released Peg. At around three o'clock in the afternoon in a cold, cloud-covered river valley, her daughter hit a patch of black ice and rolled Peg's Grand Am three times. Peg was thrown from the car and died instantly. Her daughter, and her new granddaughter were unharmed. Her fiancé, Jerry, was devastated. Death had taken her and her death was not on his tide chart.

That was the last week I wrote a fishing column. Michelle,

the new editor and I talked a few times about it but I wasn't in the mood. The day after Peg died I was supposed to go fishing with my buddy Jim. As we drove to the airport that morning the water from the bridges of the causeway looked ideal. The wind was light and variable and the weather was perfect. As the plane took off towards the connecting flight in Miami I kept thinking about how I didn't want to be flying towards my hometown for such a sad and terrible occasion. I kept wishing that my older sister had not called me the day before and that Jim and I would be hooking up linesiders down by Blind Pass by now.

As I finally walked into Barb's house up on 10th street and hugged all of those of us who were still alive I remember the river of tears streaking down our faces. A family shaken to the core by a patch of innocent ice in some late autumn river valley. There was nothing anyone could have done. No one was speeding. There wasn't any other car involved. It was just an accident that happens to someone else's family. It couldn't possibly happen to ours.

But it did. And as the tide went out all through those mournful days that followed I remembered something that I had forgotten. Our tears taste like salt water. Don't they.

Beyond Sight Of Land

*W*e are heading west on the Gulf of Mexico as these thoughts come to me. The sun is rising behind us and you can barely catch the tops of the tall, feathery Australian pines disappearing in the distance. A few minutes longer and they will vanish. Then, we will be beyond sight of land.

There is a feeling that overtakes me as we move farther and farther away from the shore that is difficult to explain to those who are afraid of going out to sea this far. I understand their apprehensions. Although I have done this a hundred times before, there is a certain element of danger to it. It is a feeling of making yourself vulnerable to the forces of nature. Putting yourself in a place where you have to be careful, in harm's way. Where you have to be attentive to the sea, the sky and, most importantly, to the wind. But it is a nature that has a cadence to it, a nature that makes sense.

This 20-foot boat has served me well before and as the three of us pound out some 18 additional miles to the west I listen attentively to the hum of the engine. I concentrate briefly but intensely on the mechanical song of gears and pistons, knowing that if something is wrong with the single engine I must hear it now, before we move too much farther out into the Gulf.

I have thought long and often as to why I choose to do this. It isn't for the catch. With the money spent on this boat and the accompanying gear I could easily purchase the fish. It's something larger than that. It's for the privilege of seeing this deep blue untouched realm. For the pleasure of experiencing first hand this last untainted kingdom left on earth: the open ocean.

Perhaps it is more than that. Perhaps beyond sight of land is beyond the sight of man. Beyond the landfills of inequities we are reminded of each and every day. To anywhere other than the daily tabloids of man's inhumanity to man. Beyond the machetes of Rwanda, the brutality and the bodies in the basement. Out here beyond the realm of man, a realm which seems to have lost its natural rhythms. A world that doesn't make sense.

Beyond sight of land is a consciousness. It is seeing the purity of the huge schools of barracuda over the wrecks and, in that sighting, somehow forgetting about the barracuda on Wall Street. Or the lobbying sharks at their tax-fed feeding frenzy in Washington, or our own petty crimes committed in every city council meeting, every calculated, white-collar handshake.

For a few brief hours I can be a child again, debate the shape of the clouds, and hear nothing more than the delicate chorus of fishing lines singing in the breeze. To breathe the salt air and enjoy this faraway place where only the sea and sky build their pure horizons.

It is more of an illusion, this vast unbroken tableland of the ocean, than it is a reality. Of this fact I am painfully aware. But what harm is there in my self-illusions? Is it not the stuff of poetry as well?

As I back off on the throttle to ease the boat down off its plane, I understand full well that we all carry our burdens, our impurities and our past with us. That who we are, this ignoble human race, can never really be left ashore. It is only an intermission. A few hours when I can avoid the endless faxes and imperatives. A brief and passing escape.

The small talk starts in as we ready the rods and break open the frozen boxes of squid. I hope the grouper are hitting today, I think to myself as I bait a hefty rod.

But then again, does it matter?

The Hangmen Of Kona

*T*o see her hanging there, thick, yellow fluids dripping from her stomach, slowly mixing with the dull red blood oozing from the hole where they stuck her with the flying gaff. The fluids slide effortlessly off her long, metallic-like bill and fall into the crystal clear waters of Hawaii. It is no longer a living thing, this once powerful marlin. It is a carcass.

The captain stands on the fly bridge, proud to have conquered this magnificent creature. Proud to have it hanging there at the stern of the boat, hanging like some criminal. But this imposing fish is guilty of no crime other than its desire to survive. Its hunger killed it, hanging there like it was lynched.

She was lynched. Lynched by a mob of anglers, all of them hungry for this prized photo-op; to be standing beside this once powerful fish, Penn International in one hand and a sign nailed into the side of his trophy saying, "588-pounds." They've waited years for this moment, anxious for their afternoon with the man in the blue suit, for their chance to catch a Pacific blue marlin.

Sadly, I was one of them. I had waited decades for my shot at catching a big blue. So there I was, at the concrete ringed harbor that had been dynamited out of the lava flows of the Big Island of Hawaii. I was in Kona, the very heart of marlin fishing, and I was thrilled to be there. But as they hoisted this 588-pound fish off the transom platform, something happened. It disheartened me to see her hanging like that, lifeless and defeated. It took away the myth.

Was it just me? The tourist from San Diego, the angler who

had landed it, seemed to be enjoying it. The cameras clicking away while he stood there, with his huge rod and reel beside his fish. Tomorrow it might be me in that viewfinder, proud of my victory. Proud to be standing beside a 14-foot-long trophy.

It was at that moment that I realized that I didn't want to kill a marlin. Yes, I still wanted to catch one, but not at the expense of its life. They are just too spectacular a creature to kill for sport. It would be like killing a snow leopard, or a jaguar. Taking the life of a beautiful creation for no other reason but vanity. If I was going to fish for marlin the following day, I promised myself that I would release my fish to fight again.

I was booked on a smaller boat the next morning. It was not an inexpensive charter, but how often would I have the chance to fish on Kona? I was there at seven. As the sun slowly rose above the 13,000-foot Mauna Kea behind us, we pulled out of the harbor. To my amazement, the skipper put the lines out once we cleared the rocks along the shoreline.

Within a block, he informed me, we were in 350 feet of water. A mile out, it was 6,000 feet deep. The base of these massive volcanoes rise two miles from the ocean floor. Once outside the harbor at Kona, you are in deep, clear blue water. Within 300 yards of the shore, you are already in marlin country.

Within minutes we had our first strike. It was amazing. The reel, which was a gold Penn 130, screamed like an alarm was going off. The line peeled off the reel at an astounding speed. After the fish had slowed its run, the mates let me take the rod out of the rod holder and carry it to the fighting chair. I had never worked a fish from a fighting chair before. As soon as the rod was firmly placed in the swivel-style holding cup at the base, the mates removed the back of the chair, put a large canvas harness on me and started clipping me to the reel.

On the other end of the line, there was a hundred and thirty-pound yellowfin tuna. A streamlined, swimming machine. I pulled back, reeled down, pulled back, reeled down for the next 25 minutes. The drag pressure on the Penn reel was set at thirty pounds, less than one quarter of the 130 pound test we were fishing with, but twice what I had ever fished with before. It was exhausting. Finally, the big tuna was alongside the stern. The gaffs sank deep into the dark red meat. The fish gate swung open and the mates pulled the tuna onto the deck. It was over.

I knew from my conversations with Robin at the charter desk, that it was the custom in Hawaii to give the catch to the captain, but I looked up and asked none-the-less, "would you mind slicing off a few pounds for my family and me to enjoy for dinner?"

"I'm afraid not. We have to sell them whole," he replied.

I figured as much, but I still felt cheated. There were over 80 pounds of fillets on this fish, I didn't think two pounds would matter. After the tuna was hurriedly smothered in ice and stuffed in a bright yellow cooler bag, we set the lines and continued on with the hunt. It was 8:30 in the morning. We had hours of trolling ahead of us and my marlin was somewhere out there.

As the hours passed that afternoon trolling, I was mesmerized by the five lures skipping across the surface of a mere breath of the largest ocean on earth, the Pacific. I couldn't help but think of my conversation with a Kona charter captain the day before. He had been fishing off this coast for 27 years.

We both leaned against the metal railing above the deck of the wharf while they raised up that huge 588-pound fish with the electric winch. He said that it was nice to see some big fish being brought in, but it was nothing like he had remembered it, back some 20 years ago.

"Back then, the enormous 'granders' were common. Times were when two or three 1,000-pound marlin might come back to the dock in any given week.

"Not any more," the captain added. "Fishing's been getting worse and worse every year now. Just can't figure it."

With his conversation still echoing within me, I went up to see the captain of the boat I was fishing on. I said that if we do hook up a big fish, and the fish was doing fine, I would like to release it. He hedged.

Remember, in Hawaii, the catch belongs to the captain. A big marlin, over 300-pounds, is worth 50 cents a pound. They smoke the flesh for marlin jerky and feed the rest of the fish to the local pigs. The smaller fish, because they are better eating, can fetch up to $1.00 a pound. Releasing a marlin for a Kona skipper is like taking a handful of $20 bills and throwing them over the side. I knew by my conversation that if we hooked a fish, my captain would keep it.

He would decide, like they often did in Kona, that it was too exhausted to release. That the sharks would get it. Besides, if they didn't keep it, the long liners 200 miles out would eventually end up with it anyway. "Those long liners, they're the ones to blame for the decline in marlin fishing these days. Not us," they were always quick to add.

From that moment on I prayed that we wouldn't catch one. I didn't want to be a party to the lynching back at the dock. The tuna was enough. I didn't hold any grudge against the man in the blue suit and I didn't feel the need to have my photo taken with one of them hanging beside me.

It felt so strange, to be trolling on a charter boat off the coast of Hawaii, fishing for a marlin, and praying to God that I wouldn't get a strike. As the hours ticked by, I knew that God had listened. We headed back to the dock without a single hit all day, except for the yellowfin and some small skipjack tuna.

There were seven or eight marlin brought in by other boats that afternoon. Some weighed 200 pounds. The largest was over 400. All of them were sold. Pig food and jerky. Cash on the line, 130-pound test line at that.

Not much is known about the marlin. How old they eventually get to be. How far they roam the deep blue Pacific. One thing that they do know is that all the big fish, all those 'granders' every boat is out there hunting, are the spawning females. They come to Kona to spawn every year around August. That's when they hold the Kona International Billfish Tournament. It is a 100 percent kill tournament.

It's not sportfishing. Not the way I read it. They have no limits, no licenses, and no resource management plan that I could find. In fact, the week I was there, the Honolulu News Press put out a front page cover story about the steady decline of Hawaii's offshore fishing. I wonder why?

The hangmen of Kona are lost. They are a commercial fishing fleet using live skipjack tuna and plastic lures for bait. They might as well use long lines. It's more efficient. The skipper told me that the reason they can keep their charters so "affordable" was because they had the right to keep and sell their catch. In the end, I would gladly pay more if I had the right to release what I wanted to release.

As it stands, I would never consider fishing in such a place again, nor recommend it to anyone. They release billfish in Cabo, in Venezuela, in Costa Rica, and their charters are every bit as affordable. In Venezuela, which presently boasts some of the best bill fishing in the entire world, a charter captain can lose his license for a year for bringing in a sailfish or a marlin.

The argument that if they don't harvest them, the long liners will, does not hold up. It becomes a Mexican standoff. No one is willing to drop their loaded gun until the fishery collapses. And collapse it eventually will. One hundred and twenty boats work the waters off Kona. Some days they take 20 marlin, others just a few. They also kill spearfish, white marlin and an occasional black marlin.

Thousands of fish are taken every year, and all of the larger ones are the very breeding stock of the fishery. Someone has to stop this slaughter. The long liners will not until they are made to. The sad part is, I doubt that the hangmen of Kona will stop the killing either.

If there is a lesson to be taken from this tale it is this; sometimes the things we dream of doing someday end up being nightmares.

I Sold My Boat

"Farewell, and forever, farewell, Cassius [Tropical Wave]!
If we do meet again, why, we shall smile;
If not, why then, this parting was well made.
Julius Caesar, Act IV, William Shakespeare

I stood on the edge of my driveway and watched as two strangers drove away with her. It was a difficult moment for me. We had been together over ten years. Ten wonderful years. Now she was leaving me. The two men who had come over the causeway to take her away were planning to tow her up north to fish the chilled waters of Lake Ontario. They lived near Watertown, New York, and the Great Lakes were in their back yard.

"Horrors!" I thought to myself as tears welled in my eyes and an overwhelming sense of loss fell upon me like a dismal, autumnal rain. I was glad that they were taking her this week. Imagine had she been parked in their yard during that terrible ice storm they had endured a few weeks ago. *Tropical Wave*, a beautiful 20-foot Mako covered in ice. My boat partially buried in a snow drift! Cruelty unimaginable.

She is a Floridian. She has never been further north than Punta Gorda, Florida. Now they were going to tow her 1,400 miles north, to an icy land filled with snow and wind chill factors - ice storms and blizzards. It was my fault. How could I let them take her from me? Why? Why? Why?

The answer was money. I needed the money. I sold my boat because I needed the money. Over the last few months I've been maintaining three boats; my new Seacat, my jon-boat and *Tropical Wave*. Three boats are too many. Every morning as I descended the stairs one of them would glance up and give me "the look." All men know "the look." Their wives practice it while they are putting on their makeup. It's the glance that slices through you like that laser in a scene from the James Bond film, *Moonraker*. It's aimed at the exact same spot.

It cuts through us like butter. You immediately go downstairs to find your crescent wrench. "OK," you announce to her, "I'll fix that dripping faucet this afternoon." She smiles.

My boats have learned how to give me "the look." I walk down the front stairs and they glance over to me saying, "What about fixing my antenna someday?"

"When are you going to rub off this ugly rust spot?"

"Can we go out for a ride today? Look how nice and calm it is." The list goes on. The honey-do list. Honey, do this. Honey, do that. You know the drill. Between the three of them, it was driving me bankrupt and timeless.

I knew that one of them had to go. With the jon-boat still covering the inshore fishing, and the Seacat better able to handle the offshore trips, it had to be the Mako.

But I never realized how painful it could be. How sad our final parting was. I know the day you buy your boat and the day you sell your boat, are supposed to be the two happiest days of your life. Not for me. I was still too emotionally attached. Co-dependent is the appropriate term.

But I will always have the memories. My first real experience at a helm. Bouncing off docks, tying off all wrong at Cabbage Key, losing my first $100 anchor. So many memories.

...The time the transom filled to the brim with water while shark fishing off the causeway. Forgetting to put the plug in by accident when we launched. Chip, my shark fishing buddy, sitting there in the stern as darkness fell over the Islands, asking me why his feet were getting wet.

The panic that ensued. Finding the plug, leaning over and anxiously screwing it in. Only to take it out again a few minutes later to drain the hull while running. Ruining both batteries from saltwater intrusion.

...Or the time in the Keys, long before I knew about Corrosion Block or T-9 aerosol spray. Diving for lobsters out of Islamorada when both of my battery cables disintegrated. Having to be towed back to shore by two old salts in a well-maintained Mako. They were amused by my lack of experience. New cables, clamps, and an entire day at the dealership. The next morning we were back at it again searching for bugs.

...Or the summer storm six years ago. Waves breaking over the bow, the wind-driven rains whipping us in the face. How *Tropical Wave* held her own against those seven and eight foot seas. Never faltering or failing us during our hour of need. A noble stance against the elements. A day never to be forgotten.

And the fish she has landed. Not to be measured in pounds, but in tons. At least 30 trips to the Keys over the decade we spent together. Dolphins by the hundred. Wahoo and rainbow runners, tuna and kingfish. Or the time my brother Steve accidently hooked a huge marlin while bringing in a schoolie dolphin. The ten-foot fish grey-hounding away with Steve's tiny dolphin while the line flew off his spool like thread on a high speed sewing machine.

And the grouper. Twenty keepers in one day, 15 in another, thousands and thousands of pounds of reds and blacks. Big grouper. Snapper and seatrout, redfish and snook, tarpon and shark and fish whose identity remains unknown. Fishes we picked up with the hook outs and dropped back into the ocean. Fish so ugly and misshapen that an angler would have to be half-mad to touch them. Squid and octopus and, yes, my father even caught a clam once from *Tropical Wave* at the causeway. A clam. We threw it back.

But now she's gone. All that remains of her are some fading photographs and a little better than $6,000 cash. It's going to be lonely here without her. I'll think of her often up there, trolling around the rivers that empty into the deep blue waters of Lake Ontario. Pulling iridescent salmon and rainbow trout up and over her graceful gunnels. Having a 12-pack of Genesee beer in her cooler and missing her ice-cold Heineken.

Catching colorful, new game-fish and riding atop clean, fresh water. No more rust spots or corrosion to deal with. It's not so bad after all, I guess. I just hope they take care of her as well as she has taken care of me. There I go again, weeping. Sympathy cards would help.

Little Fishermen

A few weeks ago John Smith, Bob Laswell and I were coming back from a washout offshore trip to the Middle Grounds north of Tampa Bay. The trip was a disaster, but that is another story. As the old Suburban rumbled and sputtered southward on I-75, the conversation wandered around to when each of us, as children, actually started fishing. Most adult anglers begin their love of fishing when they are very young, and I was curious as to when each of them had started fishing. With all three of us middle-aged and graying, it was intriguing to talk about the time when we were little fishermen.

John said that he started early, when he was just a boy. He was living in Tennessee at the time, and there was a small freshwater lake not far from his home. He and his friends used to head down to the lake to catch perch and catfish. He remembered hiking down to that lake on warm, beautiful afternoons. He loved to fish back then, and he still does.

Bob didn't fish much when he was a boy. He began his angling days after high school. He loves the ocean, and the thrill of a big hook-up as well as anyone, but for whatever the reason he was a late bloomer when it came to angling.

As for myself, I started young. Perhaps the earliest memory I have of catching fish is when I was eight. It's actually a memory of netting fish, and not of catching them by hook and line. At that time, in the late 1950s, Lake Superior had become infested with a small silvery fish not much larger than an anchovy. Their fertilized eggs had accidently entered the lake via the ballast tank of some unknown ocean freighter.

They were called smelt. Going after them with dip nets was a sport known locally as smelting.

During the evenings of late fall, just before the creeks would freeze for the winter, the smelt would spawn. Millions upon millions of smelt would run up the many streams that empty into the lake from the steep hills surrounding Duluth.

Word would soon get out that the smelt run was on and thousands of anglers would go out to the garage, get out their dusty dip nets and moldy hip boots and head out at dusk in search of their catch. At the mouth of these streams, with dip nets in hand, would soon be armies of smelt-starved Duluthians dipping downstream with the current. The dip nets had fine nylon mesh and were slightly smaller than the standard catch nets most of us carry on our fishing boats. Since the smelters were dipping with the current, catching the smelt head first as they ran upstream, it didn't take much effort. A good smelter, half in the bag from drinking a twelve-pack of Hamm's beer, could dip for hours.

Most of the time you would catch only two or three. Then you would grab the end of the net, with the little silvery smelt flittering madly about, and carefully unload it into your bucket. But at times, for biological reasons that smelters were not at all concerned with, the smelt would decide to all head up the river at once. That was when things got crazy. When the smelt all ran at once it was said that a grown man could walk across their backs to the other side of Lincoln Creek without even getting his feet wet.

At eight years of age, I believed that tale. With the smelt pouring into the creek by the thousands, the dip nets would fill to overflowing with every scoop. Five-gallon buckets would fill up in minutes. Long, skinny dip nets, straining under the weight of their catch, would buckle and collapse. Caught up in some sort of smelting frenzy, people would end up catching more smelt than was prudent. Way more.

I can remember nights when drunken smelters would fill up their car trunks with smelt. Honest. Bear in mind these were not exactly Mercedes Benz's or leather-appointed SUVs. These were Chevys and Ramblers, DeSotos and Oldsmobile 88s. These were funky cars made that much funkier by trunks full of stinking smelt and front seats that smelled like chain smoked Camels and beer.

I can remember the one night we caught so many that when we got home we soon discovered that there was no way we could ever fit our proud catch into our small refrigerator. So we put all our dead smelt in the bathtub. It looked horrible. Our old claw foot bathtub filled to the brim with smelt. In the morning we took them down to Fitchner's Meat Market to sell them to Mr. Fitchner at five cents a pound. He didn't want them. Apparently his bathtub was full of them as well. So my parents quickly invited everyone they knew in the world over for a smelt fry.

As fun as smelting was, eating them was not. You just cut off their ugly little heads and fried them. You fried them whole. They had so little in way of innards that cleaning them was futile. Their bones were so soft that once deep fried you could eat them, bones and all. Mom would dip them in beer batter, being sure to hold back a few cases of beer for the gathering crowd, fry them for a minute or two in boiling hot lard and put them on the table. They tasted like deep-fried anchovies, only with many more bones. I envied all the drunken adults at the house that night because being drunk helped make you more immune to the flavor, which was both fishy and crunchy at once.

I have other memories of fishing, and most of them are nobler than are these memories of smelting. But those are my earliest recollections of an unending fascination with things that swim.

As a footnote, the smelt no longer run in Duluth. The Minnesota Department of Natural Resources introduced Pacific salmon to eat the Atlantic smelt a few decades ago and the program was a tremendous success. The result being that the biology of Lake Superior now resembles that of a teenage chemistry experiment. A failed experiment. One that blew up the science lab. Last I checked, there were three native lake trout left, and they were going to be trapped out and transplanted to a deep lake somewhere in Arkansas. Marine biology by happenstance. Entertaining in a twisted sort of way.

But those were my earliest memories of fishing. Standing on the shores of Lincoln Creek in late October, in a cold rain, dipping up errant smelt with a bunch of drunks. Not a bad way to get introduced into the world of angling.

My tale wrapped up our conversation about little fishermen. After that, we cracked another Miller Lite, told a few more stories, and headed home. I took one last glance to the back of the Suburban just to see if there wasn't a wash tub full of smelt back there. There wasn't, but with my beer in hand, I noted how little things really change.

Big Fish Are To Die For

*T*he sun rose in a palate of oranges above the twin masts of that elegant ketch that's been anchored near the Sanibel boat ramp all winter. It looked like a postcard from Tahiti. The three of us got on board the Mako and headed to the causeway for bait. After a half dozen casts, the baitwell was teeming with nervous pilchards as we pointed the bow towards the open waters of the Gulf.

Once around the point at the Lighthouse, the broad expanse of saltwater spread out before us like an immense highway without lanes. We were free to run and, after some discussion, we decided to head to the Belton Johnson Reef to free-line our pilchards for king mackerel. Near Tarpon Beach we found ourselves confronting some large swells that had built up over the past few windy days. Aside from being slammed around a bit, the ride was slow but not unbearable. It was the ocean, and the swells were just its user fees for the three of us to pay for the luxury of being on it. The fee was nominal that morning. I've paid higher.

We were getting pounded around a bit. John and I were used to it, but Roger was not. I had recently helped Roger purchase a beautiful home in Shell Harbor and, at closing, had promised I would take him out fishing some time to show him the ropes. Roger is from the north, and he is familiar with boating so I never thought twice about how much work it is to just stand up in seven-foot swells. There is a world of difference between boating on lakes and boating on a sea. Without wind, lakes are calm. Lake boaters never really experience swells or tidal currents and, because of that, Roger was struggling just to keep his footing. John and I thought it was a bit humorous as we waited for him to find his sea legs.

Once anchored, everyone was fine. After about half an hour of heavy chumming, we got our first run. A big fish ripped out about 150 yards of line and the fight was on. Somewhere deep below us the fish managed to wrap the line around something on the bottom and despite our best efforts to chase it down, the line parted within a few minutes of the run and the fish swam off. Zero for one.

Nothing happened but telling fish stories and putting on sunscreen for the next few hours. Just before deciding to pack it in, there came a second, then a third run at once. The second turned out to be a lazy nurse shark of about 25 pounds. Boring. Cut the line. The third run was a smoker king. I set the hook and handed the rod to Roger. The battle was drawn.

It was a big, big kingfish! Roger would get it back to the boat, then off it would run. Again and again the fish would re-enact the same performance. Fifteen, 20, 25 minutes later and amidst a flurry of gaffs, blood and shouts of joy we had a 50 inch, 35 pound kingfish lying on the deck of the boat. Roger was beat.

After that, it was on to a nice tripletail, a big bonita tuna and some small black grouper. Since it was his trip, John and I let Roger haul in most of the fish we caught that day by himself. He was elated. This was fishing!

Before I finish this tale let me briefly describe Roger. It's not his real name, but that doesn't matter. Roger is in his early 60s. He's got a great smile and a disposition towards jovial. He's a bit overweight, as many of us are, and he loves a good television show, complete with caramel-covered popcorn and a Coke. You can see him, or men like him, everywhere. Slightly rotund grandfathers filling up their new cars at the 7/11, or buying donuts at the local bakery. Pick one out this afternoon. He's Roger.

We got back early and cleaned up the boat, divided up the fish and said farewell. Two days later I phoned him to ask if he and his wife had enjoyed the kingfish steaks. His wife answered the phone.

"Roger can't answer that question right now, Charlie, he's in the hospital," she replied. Apparently the combination of fighting those big fish, struggling to find his sea legs, and being out in the relentless Florida sun all day had combined to give Roger a mild heart attack that night at 4 a.m. His next ride was in an ambulance.

I was shocked. He had never complained once about being tired, or sore, or wanting to head back in. His wife told me not to feel bad. Roger's family doctor had been telling him for years to cut back on the french fries and cheeseburgers and now, after a day at sea, his steady diet of fast food calories had given him a wake-up call. It gave me a wake-up call as well.

There is an irony about getting older. You find yourself slowing down and willing to indulge yourself with good food, good wine and good fellowship. Dinner parties with great appetizers, French restaurants and cocktails on the beach. Along with the spoils of a successful career you find the unwanted notices from the bathroom scale, the high cholesterol count and shortness of breath. When you were young and hungry you were healthy and thin. Now, that you have both the time and the money, just to sit back and enjoy, maybe not.

A friend of mine once told me that the definition of middle age is when your broad mind and narrow waist change place. I think, for the most part, he was right.

Roger is OK. They kept him in the hospital for a few days, ran some tests and told him to steer clear of onion rings and to either start exercising regularly or pick out a head stone. He flew back up north a few days ago and they stuck the kingfish fillets in the freezer for now. All I could think of was what might have happened had we gone after a tarpon?

Late Summer Storm

*I*t was late in the summer, the first week of September, when the relentless grip of the Florida sun becomes overwhelming. It was the time of year when the tropical waves roll off equatorial Africa like the ancient slave ships did centuries ago. Only those dark clusters of thunderstorms hold no black men in chains, but instead come laden with a cargo of wind, rain and the seeds of the great hurricanes. It was the time of year in south Florida when the heat becomes oppressive, and the air at night seems to be spun of a steamy, black silk. I have since learned that it is a dangerous time of year to head out to sea.

I can still remember the morning sky, and the smooth ride out to my Loran fishing numbers, some 30-plus miles out in the Gulf of Mexico. The sky was low, flat and solid gray, with no sign of the thunderstorms looming above it, or the slightest hint of the coming fury it held. I have seen that same sky several times since, and it will never make such a fool of me again.

The sea itself was calm. Very calm, without a trace of wind dancing upon it. As my boat slid across the Gulf, purring smoothly at almost top speed, I noted that there were good-sized swells for such a quiet sea. They were long, rolling swells that gave us no cause for alarm.

Because of the unbroken cloud cover it was much cooler than it would have normally been this time of year. That was a welcome relief. We arrived without incident in roughly an hour of running offshore and started fishing. Within 30 minutes, John had landed a large red grouper, at least 20 pounds. Soon after that Paul had made us take note of a flock of frigate birds in the distance, diving and swooping. It was a sure sign that they were over a school of feeding pelagics. The first puffs of wind were just beginning to ruffle the morning's glassy seas.

With the grouper bite slowing down, I elected to see what the frigates were diving on. It was more than likely bonita, which are a small tuna that I like to strip and use for grouper bait. Or, if we were lucky, a school of roaming dolphin, or mahi mahi as they are called. As we neared the birds that were leading us to the fish below them, we could see the splashes and strikes of an active surface bite. We quickly put up the outriggers and dropped back the feathers and lures to have a run at whatever was on such a ravenous feed.

On our very first pass over the fish we had an immediate double hook-up. One of the two rods that had gotten smashed would not stop taking line. Within a minute's time, the lure and hundreds of yards of line were lost. On the other rod we eventually brought in the largest dolphin I have ever taken off Sanibel. Time had passed. By this time the wind was starting to stretch.

We saw several more schools of feeding fish in the distance and over the next hour the four of us managed to put six or seven big bonita in the boat. The fish were running ten pounds each and all of us were enjoying the smashing hook-ups these fish can deliver, along with their strong, driving runs.

By this time I started to realize that there must be some larger storms up there, hiding above that slate-gray sky, and they were getting ready to start flexing their muscles. Although it was not yet noon, my instincts were telling me that it was time to start easing back toward home. The sea was getting bitter, and the glass we had glided out upon was shattered with small whitecaps and numerous squall lines. The storm above us appeared to be coming from the West, so I put the compass to near ninety degrees and started running as fast as those troubled waters would allow us to back to land. We ran without incident and kept well ahead of the storm for better than five miles. Then the other storm appeared.

I know now that in the late summer, when the air is calm and the steering trade winds that blow from the southeast are in a lull, these huge thunderheads can simply make their own way. One was behind us, coming from the west like a vengeful giant, the other one was coming up from the South, as if to join his gigantic friend in this new found sport of showing four errant anglers the face of fear.

Within ten to 15 minutes the sea went mad. The down drafts from the southern storm were like chilled fists of air, slamming into the chop on our stern and making the sea confused and difficult to run on. We were trapped, cut off from shore by this massive thunderstorm, and the mood went to dead somber. Our conversations went to silence. Without hesitation all four of us donned our life jackets and waited. The seas had decided to run with the larger storm from the south and the direction of the waves turned accordingly. In no time the waves built to seven feet. The down drafts were incessant. The sound of the storm, and the lightning it carried were deafening.

But real fear is difficult to write. It is that sense you have just before the cars collide, or the doctor informs you, or you wake after the nightmare. It is intuitive, beyond the realm of our day-to-day consciousness and into the very core of our being, of our sense of life. It is ice water to the soul. It is true fright, true fear and true mortality. Your mouth becomes dry, your heart races as fast as your thoughts. You reflect on your past, think of your family, and at the same time constantly wonder if this is it...if this storm at sea is your singular mistake.

By now the waves were crashing over the bow. The bonita, which had been casually thrown into the transom some hours earlier, were now serving only to block the self-bailing scuppers valves beyond them. We found ourselves standing in ankle-deep water as Jim and Paul hurriedly threw the dead tuna back into the ocean. At the helm I soon realized that I could no longer make any headway to the East. I knew that the safe harbor of the land was twenty-five miles beyond our reach. All I could do was to point the bow of my small vessel directly into the monstrous waves, keep the motor running just above idle, and hold it steady. We all tacitly understood the depth of our danger.

Should the seas continue to build we would ultimately flip over, the bow coming up over the top of us in a rogue wave. Such a mishap would toss the four of us out there, separate and alone in an ocean gone insane. If I tried to head east, toward the shelter that Pine Island Sound would grant us, we would start taking those raging breakers on our beam and roll over and capsize within minutes. We were in trouble.

Everyone stood at the center console, white knuckled and silent. Waiting it out. I caught myself on the edge of panic, trying to think of a way out. Praying for a way out.

About that same time a Coast Guard helicopter appeared over us. My immediate reaction was to signal them somehow and tell them we were prepared to abandon ship. All I could think of was the safety of that helicopter circling above. I tried the radio, Channel 16, but with the near constant lightning strikes and the thunder around us, I could not make contact. The Loran had gone down as well. The chopper, not having heard from us, took several low passes over the boat, and seeing that we were not in imminent danger or taking on water, departed slowly to the west.

Shortly following the appearance of the chopper, a large Coast Guard plane flew over us at a very low altitude, barely visible through the driving rain and screaming winds. It looked like a ghost, or an apparition as it emerged and disappeared again into the blankets of clouds above. I have since learned that it was marking our position just in case.

To this day I am not sure that the better decision would not have been to send up a signal flare to the helicopter and give that 20-foot boat back to the sea. But for some reason the four of us decided to ride it out. Then, as if by making that decision, it gave all four of us some new-found courage. Everyone started to relax. Nothing outwardly had changed. The waves were approaching eight feet, the wind was gusting to 40 knots, and we were drenched to the core with a combination of saltwater spray and the freshwater rain. But something was different.

It was apparent to all of us that everything was holding steady. The storm was no longer building and the boat was performing perfectly. With the scuppers open and the standing water, along with its accompanying weight, now gone, the waves were coming over the bow with far less frequency. After an hour of facing southward into the gale, I was ever so cautiously able to inch our heading back toward the east. The next 15 miles took another two hours to navigate. By the time we made it to the welcome luxury of a tide-rippled pass, some three and a half hours had gone by. We were then safely on the other side of the storm, and as we crossed the still choppy waters of the bay, all of us were glad to be so close to where we belong. Land.

We were later to learn that two boats were beat up quite badly out there, and one of them had sent the SOS to the Coast Guard. No one was lost that day on the Gulf, but that was an arbitrary choice. Otherwise, this tale might have read like an obituary.

It was a late summer storm at sea. A singular lesson in the frailty of a small boat beneath the power of these huge thunderstorms. The fear itself is gone, but the taste of it remains in my heart from that afternoon on, and will never fade. It will never be as calm as it was that morning for me again. Hopefully, I will never be that far from shore again.

Of Manatees And Microprocessors

We call them sea cows. They are also called manatees. I see them while fishing in the Jon-boat. In a world of microprocessors and satellite telecommunication they seem absurdly inefficient. Lumbering along, slow and seemingly dim-witted, they appear childlike in their goliath innocence. We feel this urge to protect them, to make room for them amidst our jet skis and 200-horse power flats boats. So many of them have died over these last few weeks that we feel responsible. Nature can be so cruel to the inefficient. We feel helpless. We slice them up, post mortem, looking for a reason. The image haunts us. Scientists wearing thick glasses holding up manatee livers, wanting to find out why they've been dying off? Extinction is such a terrible, terrible word.

They are not the real sea cows. The real sea cow was the Stellar sea cow. It is extinct. It was closely related to the manatee, but far larger. It lived in the Bering Straits near Kamchatka in the far northeastern corner of Russia. The Stellar sea cow was first discovered in 1741. It was gone by 1768. The Russian sealers and fur hunters ate them all. They grew to a length of over 24 feet and weighed as much as a small whale.

They were plentiful when they were first discovered, grazing like oceanic elephants on the rich seaweed that flourished in the sheltered bays of the Bering Islands. Like the manatee, they were very, very easy to harpoon and devour. From the logs of the whaling ships, it was noted that they tasted like pork.

I wrote the following poem in 1972. I could have written it

yesterday. It has a surface humor to it but it addresses a deeper issue.

Don't feel helpless. Don't just stand there like there isn't a damned thing you can do, because there is something you can do. There is nothing left for us to do for the original sea cows. We ate them out of the ballpark. But the manatees will get through this bout they are having because of the red tide and they will hopefully bounce back. Help them do that by contributing and participating. Buy yourself a manatee plate next time you replace your license plate. Make a donation to a wildlife rehabilitation center, to Mote Marine up in Sarasota (They treat injured manatees) or simply slow down the next time you are running inshore.

Recycle. Never throw out any fishing line, stop and pick up that plastic soda bottle you walk by every morning on the beach and throw it away. I know it wasn't you who tossed it there to begin with but what difference does that make? It wasn't you who barbecued up the last Stellar sea cow. It isn't you who's killing the manatees out in Pine Island Sound.

But it is all of us who share this environment in the end isn't it? If there is something you can do today to improve the health of our world, do it. Here then, is the poem I promised you.

Da dodo he done be no mo'

Cluck, cluck, cluck
Doodle dee dee dee dee dummmmm da.....
Kerplunk, kerplunk, kerplunkadoo.....

He done
do not so good dat bird.
Hugh?
He done be no mo'.

Cooo, cooo, cooo, big chicky chicky
Pigeon bird,
He gone away, fa, fa away.

(But he tastum' sooooooo goooooood!)

He easy catchum you see,
He no can fly.
Flop, flop, floppin'
So he tastum, yum, yum, yum, sooooooo goooooood.

You watchum, smart modern man.
Cluck, cluck, clucka, coooooooo.

O' you done be dat dodo.

And you listenum, great modern man.
Du, du, da chicka, chicka cooooo.
(but boy, o' boy, o' boy, fo' a littl' while he tastum' so
awful gooooood!)

And you listenum hard, big modern man.
Cause da dodo was just da first nail.
Plucka, plucka, plucka poooooohhhhh....
(O' he never gunna be no mo', no mo', no never again,
Cause he done be esstinct, shur'nuff)

An it's a darn big coffin' dat you be buildin'.

1972

'Bout This Time

*F*or weeks the wind has been pouring up from the south. My boat sits on its trailer and waits. It has more patience than I do. We cannot go offshore in these conditions and both of us know it. Across the open waters the seas have become wild, intoxicated with the howl of 20-knot breezes. I tune in to NOAA weather radio only to have some computerized voice out of Ruskin, Florida remind me, "From Cape Sable to Tarpon Springs, small craft should exercise caution." I turn the radio off. I can see the tops of the Australian pines whipping in the gusty breezes, pointing north, northwest. The pines confirm what the monotone voice on my VHF radio has warned: exercise caution.

It's like this every spring, although following such a wet and windy winter, it seems worse this year. It is worse. Unable to take the boat out, I settle for cleaning up some of my rods and reels, doing odd jobs around the house and waiting. Waiting for the winds to die. Waiting for the first big thunderstorms to build over Clewiston, signaling the beginning of the rainy season here in south Florida.

As I begin removing reel handles and cutting off rusty hooks, I silently reminisce. I remember a time when this same wind, stretching from Destin, Florida, to International Falls, Minnesota, meant everything to me. The south wind. The end of winter. How I used to wait for it to finally arrive when I lived up in northern Minnesota. Waiting through another cold and brutal winter for those warm gusts to work their way up along the Mississippi River valley. Waiting for the ice to break, to find the rivers and creeks rushing with the melting snow pack. Waiting for the loons to return home.

In my imagination, I want to follow this south wind. I want to vanish into it, disappear into the scent of Peach blossoms in Georgia. I want to blow north with it, watching it transform the wasteland back into the lush, green America that is spring. To race across the unplowed fields of Kansas, the flat expanses of Iowa and beyond. Stretching all the way to the vast wheat fields of Manitoba.

And as I envisioned this picturesque journey, I thought of the fishermen along the way. I thought of how they welcomed this south wind. How much it means to them. I saw them in the back yard, uncovering their shiny Bass Tracker from that dark blue cover they ordered from Cabela's catalog last fall. Anxious to try their new Shimano reel out on some hungry Alabama largemouth bass. Anxious for the big females to start bedding up to spawn.

Or further north, near Lake of the Ozarks, where some old timer is busy putting new spark plugs in his 30-year old Johnson outboard. "Why buy a new one, when this old thing runs just fine," he mumbles to himself. "If I can get her started, that is."

He's been anticipating this south wind for months. Waiting for the crappies to put on the feed. Waiting for the dogwoods to bloom, and the rivers to run thick with catfish and smallmouth bass.

I wanted to soar on that wind, all the way back home to Duluth, Minnesota. Back to opening day of trout season. The pussy willows blossoming as some solitary fly fisherman works his way upstream. His casts are rusty but his enthusiasm is as fresh as the breeze. A rainbow breaks for his fly, then, at the last instant, falls away. Perhaps tomorrow he will take that hand-tied mayfly.

Then to continue riding that warm air north. Onward to the Lake of the Woods. Watching two young guys rolling their 16-foot aluminum Lund over after being buried in three feet of snow all winter. Hooking up their new 40-horse Mercury and getting their dusty tackle out from the corner of the basement. Spinners and strip-ons, bobbers and wire hooks designed for leeches. Tackle designed for walleye country. Six-packs of Hamm's beer and pick up trucks rusted around the running boards.

I could be there on opening day. Alarms going off at 5:00 a.m.

Drowsy anglers rustling about in dark kitchens, looking for their first cup of joe. Stopping by to pick up Rudy, then the long drive out to the lake. Pulling into Ralph's Bait and Tackle for some night crawlers and leeches. Maybe a tip or two from Ralph himself on what colors are working this year. If anyone knows what colors are working this spring, it's Ralph.

As they pull away, still groggy but becoming excited with the thought of getting back out on the water, you can almost hear the conversation.

"We'll have to stay close to the south shore and work that rocky point just this side of where Kettle Creek comes in. With this gusty wind and all," says Rudy.

His partner merely nods. He's too darned sleepy to say much. Meanwhile, a country western station plays on the truck's inexpensive radio. As they near the lake, the music begins to break up. No one bothers to look for another station.

The wind is from the south, and I want to ride upon it. Although it keeps me safely ashore here in Florida, I remember how much it meant to me over a decade ago when I still lived back up in Duluth. How it pushed the last chunks of ice back out across Lake Superior. How we waited for months for this wind and how we loved that day when it finally arrived. The day it whipped up the dusty streets. The afternoon it melted the last few clumps of grainy snow that stubbornly hid in the shadows between the houses. The morning it begged the lilacs into bloom.

As I rode that wind, I longed for the sweet scent of those lavender lilacs. I wanted to see the dandelions pushing up from the thawing yards. I watched the old salt in Missouri finally get his Johnson started. "I hope the crappie are biting," he said to his aproned wife when he went back in to kiss her goodbye.

"They do every year 'bout this time, don't they Hank?" She reassured him. She was right. They do every year "'bout this time." Springtime that is.

The Wind In The Lines

*T*he lion of winter is upon us. The cold fronts sweep down weekly in a familiar pattern. The wind from the last front pours up from the south accompanied by the memoirs of summer. Temperatures climb into the low eighties as the humidity tries to take Florida hostage again. But it's February and the sun doesn't have the muscle it has in August. It stalls.

Then, as if on cue, another cold front spills out of northern Canada and rushes wildly into the moist, tropical air. When they collide, the cold dry air squeezes out the moisture like a windy giant wringing out a gray, wet towel. Once done, the giant marches southward toward Cuba, leaving us clear, cold and sunny.

With a fresh cold front fast upon us, an old friend and I went out fishing last weekend. We got under way with a 15-knot north wind pouring down the coastline of western Florida and the whitecaps sparkling on the Gulf. It was cold. The air was clean and crisp, as if God had just changed the sheets of the world. The color of the water was as blue as a postcard from Greece. It was a fine day to be alive.

It was just the two of us and we started well past noon. Neither of us had the nerve to set out on the water with the air temperature still under 50 degrees. We have long since acclimated to the islands, both of us convinced that all land north of the Mason-Dixon line should be declared uninhabitable. Florida boys. Southerners.

We were going after kingfish, at least in theory. We had cast net up a livewell full of white baits at the causeway bridges and we had rigged our lines with wire before getting under way. We looked the part.

After rounding the point by the lighthouse, both noting the absence of swimmers or sunbathers, we headed west, northwest toward an artificial reef. Perhaps we would find a school of king mackerel there.

In less than half an hour we were securely anchored up not far from the marker buoy, our chum bag hanging over the side and our four spinning rods soaking the live minnows off the stern. The wind was to our backs and behind the modest wind break of the center console, it was almost warm. The slanted sunlight of a mid-winter sun kept the chill out as we began our conversation.

My friend had been having woman troubles. He'd been divorced for two years now and he was back into the dating game. His first marriage had been a dead end, and their divorcing, in this case, was the right decision for him to make. But he was lonely.

He had just been shut out by another woman whom he felt he was in love with and he wanted to know why. I wasn't much help. I know a lot more about king mackerel fishing than I do about women and I would be the first to admit it.

There is nothing more confusing to comprehend than a woman's behavior, and you can tenfold that when the woman involved is angry and disappointed in you. All I could do that afternoon was listen. Maybe that was all I needed to do.

So we talked.

We talked as the afternoon sun lost its weak winter grip on zenith and slid silently toward the horizon. We talked about love, about children, about having money and not having money. We talked about being heartbroken and about breaking hearts. We talked about life. We talked like grown men so seldom do.

Our fishing rods sat motionless, as though they were so engrossed in our conversation that they dared not interrupt us. What would the crashing strike of a smoker kingfish be at this moment other than an unwanted annoyance? Having to suddenly reel the other lines in, scrambling for the gaff, screaming and carrying on. Who needed it?

We weren't fishing to be fishing. We were sitting on this anchored raft in the middle of the ocean with the north wind to our backs and a flock of seagulls and a setting sun to our south. We were wrapped up in a conversation that mattered a thousand times more than some overexposed photo of a stringer full of mackerel. Our fishing that afternoon was little more than the sound of the wind in the lines. The distant song of a north wind playing against the 20-pound monofilament. That was all it needed to be.

Eventually the conversation wore itself out. My friend had some tough decisions ahead of him. If he really loved her, then time and that love should bring them back together. There was nothing I could add to that but a willingness to hear him out. As the sun got down to that place where it no longer held any trump cards against the hand of spades held by that north wind, we pulled our anchor and motored back toward the dock. We didn't catch anything.

It was a great day of fishing. The wind in the lines, what a glorious sound it is.

Beyond El Niño

*L*ast Saturday we tried to get offshore to do some grouper fishing. We almost made it to a rock pile I have the coordinates for 6 miles out of Redfish Pass. The wind kept building all morning and as the Mako pounded farther and farther out to sea, it became obvious that we were going to have to turn back. The wind was hitting 15-knots when my father-in-law started feeling queasy and my back began aching from the relentless slamming of the bow. We were back in the shelter of the passes before 10 a.m. The fishing trip was canned. El Niño was at it again.

The swales along Periwinkle, filled to overflowing with rainwater, remind all of us who are living here on Sanibel this winter (1998) that something is akimbo. Where is the cold, crisp air rushing out of Canada every week? Where is the white washing air, painting this peninsular Florida in sunlight? Isn't this supposed to be our dry season? The time of year where we beg for an occasional shower while the six o'clock newscaster hints of impending water restrictions and brush fire hazards.

Not this year. This year, they tell us on the evening news, this year is the return of the Christ Child, El Nino. The huge Pacific storms slam into California, then splinter and reform as powerful lows just off Texas. The storms regroup over the Gulf of Mexico and then turn their damp sights on Florida. Our winter becomes wet and insufferable, like a bad summer in Maine. All because of a warm body of Pacific ocean water due west of Mexico.

It has started me thinking about the power of natural forces.

My first inclination is to pin the blame on global warming. I did a quick C.I. check to measure my personal contribution to the greenhouse gases. For those of you unfamiliar with the term, "C.I.", it's an acronym for "cylinder index." They use it up in Minnesota as a twisted barometer of masculinity.

To arrive at your C.I., take all your gasoline powered devices, both two-stroke (lawn mowers, hedge trimmers, boat motors) and four-stroke (automobiles) engines, count the total number of cylinders in your possession and you arrive at your C.I.. Mine is presently at 27. Real men like to hang near 50.

Then I reconsidered. What if El Niño doesn't have anything at all to do with global warming. What if it's just another natural occurrence, like tornadoes, droughts, or typhoons. Having a high C.I. doesn't help matters much. It certainly gets expensive, if for no other reason than the high cost of all those spark plugs, but is it causing the Pacific Ocean to overheat?

The greater question here is how much control do we have over the tremendous forces of nature? We think that we are in control. It wasn't that long ago that we thought the earth was flat. We were absolutely positive that we were the center of the universe and everything revolved around us. The Hubble keeps rubbing our little snouts in those theories with every passing snapshot. The earth isn't flat and those "billions of billions" of galaxies out there, they're not exactly hanging on our next lamebrained explanation of them.

The truth is painful. We are not driving. We are passengers. There are forces at play that imperil our meager fiefdom daily. How many particulates are heaved into the atmosphere with every Pinatuba or Krakatoa? When will the next meteor or comet slam into this planet? Or an unknown virus ravage our population? Our fingers are, for the moment, off the nuclear trigger, but there are far more sinister threats out there over which we have absolutely no control.

We are not at the helm. We are mere passengers on spaceship Earth. Hopefully, you're enjoying the ride.

Don't misunderstand me. This essay isn't intended as an excuse. Environmentalism is a personal commitment. All of us should do what we can to lower our C.I., recycle and improve our environment. What

I'm addressing here is this mass illusion we have of our own self-importance. Like the dinosaurs, we are convinced that our kingdom is invincible. The crater buried deep beneath the ruins of the Yucatan should remind us of our status on the bus. The destination unknown, the scenery spectacular and the road given to lapses of chaos. Things change quickly down here folks, so remember to keep your tickets handy.

It's easy to understand the root of our delusion. We're the only ones presently capable of telling ourselves about our self-importance. That's like the pot calling the kettle black. I haven't come across too many extra-terrestrial reviews of the human race lately. Besides, we know that they would pan the show, even if they found the comedy routine unequaled in the universe.

No, I doubt that mopeds are causing El Niño. I refuse to blame the wind on the Chernobyl disaster or the rains that fall on the side effects of bovine flatulence. It would be nice to keep it all that simple. But it's not that simple. Ice ages come and they go. The wind blows and it ceases. The rain falls and the rain stops falling. History bears this out repeatedly.

Passengers on a big, round bus. God is driving.

This Last Week

*I*didn't fish at all last week. My rods and reels languished in the corner of the storage shed, looking like old golf clubs. The kind of outdated clubs you find at garage sales. Rusty seven irons and split three woods with weather-cracked grips. Clubs and putters that haven't graced a fairway or a green since 1984. They're priced at $5 each but, hey, make me an offer.

My Seacat was parked in the repair shop, getting its second engine rebuilt, but that wasn't the reason I didn't wet a line either. I have a second, inshore boat that's working fine. I know that the snook are biting and the redfish, well, the redfish are hitting everywhere. I know that there are cobia at the causeway, pompano on the beach and massive tarpon prowling Tarpon Bay. And I know how to catch all of them.

This last week I didn't fish because I didn't want to fish. My father flew down from Minnesota with my young nephews, Arion and Ty, and I wanted to spend some time with them. My dad and I played cribbage, chatted a bit about family and friends, and spent our time together as freely as lotto money won by a double-wide owner in St. Petersburg. Over the weekend all of us, Molly, the four boys and I went down to the seaside to soak in a pool and walk the beach. My father won at cribbage. He always does.

That was enough.

About ten days ago, on my way to an appointment, I was in an accident on Periwinkle. I had stopped behind someone turning into the Jacaranda restaurant for lunch when a tourist driving a Dodge minivan rear-ended me. As fate would have it, I happened to glance at my rear view mirror an instant before the impact. That car's going to hit me, I remember thinking to myself seconds before the collision. It did. No squealing brakes, no warning, and absolutely nowhere for me to go. The thud had that inevitability quality to it. Like taxes and that other inevitability we try to ignore.

Aside from some whiplash that has me searching for industrial strength Advil and some minor damage to my Land Cruiser, nothing more should come of it. It was more of a tap than a car wreck. But that tap was a reminder. A reminder of just how quickly things can change in life.

With the memory still fresh in my thoughts, I realized that fishing is a luxury of time. When we feel comfortable with the world, we find the time to enjoy it. We relax, head out to fish, to golf, play tennis, garden, sew, or do whatever we find pleasurable. But we should never become so engrossed in our pastimes to lose perspective. Only a fool has that much time.

When something comes along and unravels us, reminding us of how fleeting our existence is, we should pay attention. That minivan tap on my shoulder reawakened me to what really matters. There is a time to set down your spinning reels, your *Wall Street Journal* and your television remote. For in the end, what do we really have? Toys? Money? These are things. They are as cold and as lifeless as stone.

What we really have is each other. A kiss beside the surf, a game of cards with your aging father, the laughter of my boys playing with their cousins on a rope swing in the woods. Friends, family, and the endless rituals of generations passing, passing, passing. To where? We don't know. From where? We don't know.

How can we know? Such a meager stretch of eternity belongs to you and me. Some 70, 80 years at best. A tiny, tiny window looking out across the enormous landscape of eternity. All of us live with this uncertainty. If you pause for a moment and let these words remind you of it, you will understand what it is I am trying to say.

So when that next tourist hits you on Periwinkle, or the doctor closes the door behind him with your foreboding test results, or when you get that call in the night, the one that comes too late to be good news, remember to let your fishing rods and golf clubs gather cobwebs in the corner. Take your wife to dinner. Call an old friend you've been holding a grudge against. Give yourself away. And if you have some time to spare after that, write a letter or send an e-mail to God. He checks his mail regularly and he always writes back.

Good luck fishing this week.

Selected Tales
(1971-2001)

Author's Notes

In 1972 I self-published a collection of prose and poetry entitled, *Untitled*. The work was 100 pages long and there were 1001 printed. The books sold well and only a very few of them are still around.

Some of the works included in this section are originally taken from *Untitled*. Those include *The Man Who Lived In A Hole* and *To Irving Who Vanished*. Some of the poetry in the following section was also taken from *Untitled*.

During the same time period I was writing a weekly column for the *UMD Statesman*, which was the collegiate rag at the University of Minnesota, Duluth. The column was called the *Universe Wisdom Lectures*. They were precocious to put it mildly.

The one *Universe Wisdom Lecture* included here, *Make A Big Splash, Or Group Suicide, A Novel Group Therapy*, was heavily influenced by the war in Vietnam, which was in full swing at the time. The madness of that war left a lasting impression on anyone who was a part of my generation. It was a time of turmoil in America, a time of rebellion and anger. It will never make sense.

The other works were in small, unpublished collections that I assembled in the '70s. At the end of every year I would collect all of my writings, selecting those I felt were worthy and bind them together in three ring folders. *Closetbeard* was one such collection. From it I elected to include a story called *The Mad Bicycler*.

There is also the epilogue from my last novel, *Way Under Contract, a Florida Story*, included in this section. That epilogue sums up my feelings about how unjustly we treat our fellow creatures down here on planet earth. To date, because of the $1 per copy commitment from the sale of *Way Under Contract*, thousands of dollars have been donated to the Sanibel Captiva Conservation Foundation (SCCF). Hopefully it has helped and will continue to help for years to come.

Charles Sobczak
August, 2001

The Man Who Lived In A Hole

*P*eople would get bored while driving around on a late Saturday night and head down to Railroad Street to visit the man who lived in a hole. The hole was a few paces west of the Woodruff pulp plant chain link fence and a few paces east of the Duluth Mesabi and Iron Range railroad tracks. It was a good spot for a hole.

There was a convenient gravel road running along the tracks where the people who drove down to visit the man who lived in a hole could park. Once positioned correctly, they would flash their lights or honk their horn until the man who lived in a hole would come out of his hole. He would slide back the wooden doors that covered his sad shelter, stand up, smile and wave to his fans. Sometimes the people in the cars would throw him an orange or a candy bar. The man who lived in the hole never looked very good, wearing dirty clothes and sporting an ill-kempt, salt-and-pepper beard.

It soon became a small weekend theater that opened after the bars closed, when no one had anything else to do. The entire performance would last as long as it took the old man who lived in the hole to crawl out and give his audience a big smile. Everyone was glad to see him, and, over time, he eventually became the odd, midnight centerpiece in this otherwise dull town.

Nobody was really bothered by what was going on and occasionally, on week nights, the local police would come down to check up on his health. He lived in his hole all that summer using cardboard boxes for blankets and old grain elevator doors to cover the top of the hole when it rained.

But the man who lived in a hole only lived there for two summers because in August of the second year one of the midnight visitors was from the Board of Health and they didn't think it very suitable to let people live in holes. Even if they wanted to.

Untitled, 1973

All Across My Shoulders

"For fathers are the keepers
of the key.
Father, to son, to eternity."

*W*hat am I to do? In a few hours' time the sun will labor its way above the still damp horizon and soon thereafter you will awaken. I stand beside your bright blue crib, listening to your gentle breathing in the silence of this warm Florida morning. I thought that I had heard you cry out. So I awoke from a restless sleep and came into your bedroom to comfort you.

Now, as I stand beside you, looking upon your light-blond hair and your mother's fair skin, I wonder if it wasn't the child deep within me who cried out. Who asked me to come to your bedside in this faint pre-dawn light asking, what am I to do?

It is so difficult to know what is asked of me. You are turning two soon, and the world around you is unfurling before your eyes in a collage of changes. I long to look back and read from the manual my father passed to me but the pages are worn and the key passages are lost. What little I can decipher from that tired manual is thick with the smell of brandy and broken promises.

"For fathers are the keepers
of the key.
Father, to son, to eternity."

What am I to do? With only this tattered guide left to turn to. Your hazel brown eyes are just becoming aware, while my tired eyes look for something familiar in a fatherhood I know so little of. Where my memories of dad are wrought with pain...pain measured in the hourglass of my own lost youth. Memories of us bending over that hot air vent on the second floor in that run-down house on Michigan Street listening to them fight.

Listening to him cursing mom. The two of them fighting late into that poor, poor white-trash night. Wondering why? But we never understood why. We were, my brothers and I, too wrapped up in the cocoon of innocence to ever know why. Thirty years have passed and I still do not know why.

But what of this time? My first son, soon awaiting his first few words of guidance from me. Words of guidance I still long to hear from my father's lips, though the decades bear grim testimony that those words will never come.

"For fathers are the keepers
of the key.
Father, to son, to eternity."

Thinking back, remembering. Recalling all those years that my mother suffered so. Pouring everything she had into us. Trying desperately to keep us from drowning in that sea of malice. Giving us everything she had until that day came when she was finally emptied, taken by ambulance to the hospital with her first nervous breakdown. The first of many more to come.

And although her unending wellspring of love saved us, it was never the same as a father's advice. Advice that was never given. Instead we were left with the sound of swearing and the slamming of the front door as dad went down the street to get drunk again. As drunk as his paycheck would allow.

So no wonder now, in these early hours of the morning, that these secret fears within me begin to wake. The secret cries that bring me here, carefully covering you up against the dampness. A dampness so heavy that it frightens me to my very soul in this, the passing of the torch.

I can only pray that by remembering my life without a father I can somehow keep myself from repeating that maligned past. That I can break this chain. This chain of fools. That I can stand here, as the sun climbs the arch of the east, and in my unheard whisper say, "That I love you, Logan, and I wish for you the best."

"For fathers are the keepers
of the key.
Father, to son, to eternity."

Winter, 1990

At Christopher Boland's Cabin

*L*ike a distant ghost these images still linger within me of the great river and the unbroken forests of the Yukon. Recalling clearly that afternoon the three of us, Patricia, Brian and I, paddled our canoe out of the main current and searched along the edges of that powerful stream for a place to camp. Those moments, still frozen in my thoughts, asking me to write this brief memoir. Asking me to re-sketch in words the three days we spent that late August of 1971 at Christopher Boland's Cabin. How we discovered it, enjoyed it and eventually left it for the world beyond the vastness that is the Yukon Territory.

As darkness gathered that night, we pulled our aluminum canoe off toward the western shoreline of the river, searching for a deserted settlement called the Yukon Crossing. There, some 70 years ago, a ferry brought thousands of young men and supplies across the quarter-mile wide river. They were all headed to seek their fortunes in the newly discovered gold fields of the Klondike. Men like Robert Service, Jack London and the fictitious Sam McGee, all of them finding adventure and, if they were lucky, unearthing the motherlode.

But the spruce and poplar forest had long since reclaimed the old Dawson Trail. From our vantage point some 20 feet from shore we saw no trace of Yukon Crossing, nor of any deserted cabin where we might have hoped to camp that night. As the twilight that lingers for hours in the land of the midnight sun grew slowly dimmer we continued down river. Our bones aching from paddling over 40 miles that day. Our hopes fading in the dying light. Twenty minutes later we saw a cabin tucked in amidst the thick alder brush and willow. We pulled the canoe along the muddy bank and walked up the low lying bank to see if it was deserted.

It wasn't a very large cabin, maybe 20 feet long and a dozen wide. Its spruce logs had weathered and sagged with the passing decades, giving the place a crooked, graying look. Like an old man standing on the shore of life. The roof was low and covered with a foot of sod, helping to insulate it against the brutal winters that often fell to 60 below zero. It had a small porch out front where an old rocking chair still sat beside a small stack of split firewood. The overgrown front yard held two large caches of split wood that were once intended to take the owner through another winter, but they were wet and slowly rotting back into the soil.

The cabin had a feel to it. It spoke of long nights decades past where rugged, bearded men drank shots of whiskey and spun yarns of wolves, gold and families left behind. Wintry nights, where the wood stove burned feverishly in its efforts to stave off the bitter cold beyond.

But Brian and I were soon disappointed to find that the front door was still padlocked shut. We would have to move on down the river, pushing further and further into the descending twilight. Before leaving, Brian had decided to check the back side of the log cabin. There, he found that the back door was wide open. Peering in, he could see that it had long since been visited by bears, varmints and weary river travelers like us. We called back to Patricia that it was deserted and smiled. We would spend the night here.

We hurriedly picked up the cabin, unrolled our sleeping bags, jammed the back door shut, and fell asleep amidst the silence of the wilderness surrounding us. In the morning, Patricia cooked incredibly delicious pancakes on the beautiful old wood stove that still worked perfectly. There was a fine oak desk where many a long letter had been written to loved ones back home during the eight months of winter that engulf this hard land.

After breakfast, we spent the balance of the morning cleaning up the mess of years of abandonment. It was then, from reading the scattered letters and notes, that we learned that the cabin was last lived in by a man named Christopher Boland. From these same letters we discovered that he was a geologist from Winnipeg. His wife Susan was born in the United States and she was staying with him in the cabin that summer. She must have been a good cook, judging from the large assortment of spices we found near the cook stove.

Christopher was also an artist and a writer and not very fastidious about paying his bills. It looked as though they had journeyed here in search of minerals for some mining firm back east. The cabin had not been used except by an infrequent wanderer or an errant wild animal in ten years. By the tone of the collection letters we found, Mr. Boland didn't have much luck finding whatever ore he was searching for. Nor did most of the men who had come to the fabled Klondike searching for gold 60 years before him.

But we were not searching for gold, or nickel, or ore of any kind. Brian and I soon tired of playing detective and decided to head out to the front porch that afternoon to play some cribbage. The sun was lingering in the west as we dealt hand after hand in the cool, August air. Brian won.

We had decided early on, after six long days on the river, to spend a second night in this inviting shelter. We had a stove to cook on, mattresses to sleep on, and we could sleep the night without having to fear some grizzly bear wreaking havoc with our food supplies.

But there was one more thing about Christopher Boland's cabin, something that I find difficult to explain. Something that stands apart from the three nights we eventually ended up spending there. Three nights in a deserted cabin on a 700 hundred mile canoe trip down the Yukon River.

Because at Christopher Boland's cabin you can walk but a few feet and be standing on the Yukon's banks. At this small house with four-foot doorways you can do nothing at all and feel certain that you are doing the right thing. At this cabin in the heart of the coldest land in America you can watch the northern lights shimmer across the August night sky. You can sit on the tilted porch and whittle a birch branch away without expecting company. You can step outside and holler as loud as possible with no reply but that of a mountain's distant echo. You can fish grayling in a stream a half-mile away or hunt rabbits in your back yard at midnight. At Christopher Boland's cabin you can pretend.

The entire nightmare of this 20th century can slip away to nothingness while a coffee cake bakes in the oven and Brian and I play a second round of cribbage. At this crooked log cabin on the edge of eternity you can disappear into a world that could be today or a hundred years ago. A place where a cease-fire is called amidst the madness of our planet and for three glorious days you can breathe in slowly enough to savor the clean, crisp air that surrounds you.

Three days of pause where time isn't pounded out with the hammering of a thousand clocks and a series of unending appointments. In that cabin a hundred miles from anywhere there was suddenly wilderness once again. A land where moose and grizzly still share the world with us. Where the forest stretched on and on, unbroken by footsteps or highways for hundreds of miles in any direction.

For three glorious days at Christopher Boland's cabin the earth became itself for the very first time in my life. At that small hand-hewn shelter miles and miles from the incessant noise of progress I grew alive and aware. For the briefest of moments I saw everything ancient and modern at once. I saw Christopher painting in this overwhelming quiet while, far beyond, subways howled beneath the streets of New York City. I saw Patricia putting wood in the cook stove while men somewhere in the world beyond mounted machine guns on halftracks, anxious for the next battle.

I saw the wild and the civilized spinning in this passage of time. I saw the youth beside the aged. I saw with a clarity rare and frightening at once.

At Christopher Boland's cabin you can sleep without the secret fear of waking.

Summer, 1971

The Mad Bicycler

*H*e was a signpost, or a mailbox, or an aluminum culvert draining an unnamed muskeg creek. He was as much a part of this rolling county highway as were the potholes. And like those potholes, he was equally unpredictable.

Two weeks might pass by without so much as a glimpse of him and then, seemingly out of nowhere, he would reappear. It might be two in the morning, in a drenching rain, or it might be four-thirty in the afternoon under clear, sunny skies. Not having any clue as to why the old man behaved the way he did, we had decided that he was mad. That he was off his rocker, three cards short of a full deck, a quart low.

I still know nothing about his past, his name, or how he had come to behave so crazily. All I knew of him was what I had chanced to gather while driving past him on this uncrowded country road.

He looked like a poor old man, in his late 60s. There was nothing in his appearance that would set him apart from any other old man, except the haggard condition of his clothes. He wore the dark brown pants and red flannel shirts common to the second-hand stores of northern Minnesota. Most of the time he never wore a cap, but on cold summer nights I would note that he would sometimes wear a plain gray knit cap. He reminded me of one of those retired old men who always gather around the demolition of old hotels downtown. The kind of old men who remember back when that hotel was "The place to stay."

No, the man pushing the bicycle was nondescript for the most part. It was his bike that always caught your eye. It was a huge farm bike, with enormous fenders and a hefty steel frame. It was painted a flawless sky blue and came adorned with all the reflectors, headlights and baskets one would expect from such a classic. It was a "takes-two-to-lift-it bike."

The tires on it were encyclopedic, looking more as though they had been made for a small motorcycle than for a pedaling machine. The overall impression that his bicycle left on you was one of longevity. It was a "they sure don't make them like they used to" bike. But that enormous bike complemented the old man in a stunning, if unconventional way. Always rolling beside him like a diamond in a coal mine. A pair of perfectly mismatched antiques.

Perhaps the thing that made me think he was mad was that I never once saw him riding his big, blue bike. For over two years all I ever saw him do was walk it. Patiently stroll this heavy sky-painted bike down the highway's gravel shoulder. In the dead of winter, in a dense fog, on a hot summer's day or in the middle of the night, he would suddenly appear. Pushing his two-wheeled bicycle with a slow, steady pace.

Sometimes he would be heading in towards town, sometimes heading out. I always thought that he simply had to ride it sometime. Maybe he got on it only when he felt that there was absolutely no chance of traffic coming. He might have been trying to avoid annoying those drivers who get nervous when they have to pass someone riding a bike down a narrow county highway. Maybe he had lost his sense of balance.

In the end, it was easier to say that he was mad. Oh, not mad mad, hysterical and dangerous. He was old-man mad. A gray and brown flannel mad. A harmless, patient insanity that walks his heavy steel frame bike up and down a lonely stretch of highway.

There were, of course, stories about him. Stories that surrounded his madness like scouts surround their first big campfire. Once, on a cold New Year's Eve in 1971, a partied-out carload of us were driving out to the cabin and found him silently walking his blue bike over the packed snow along the shoulder in 10-below weather. It was almost three in the morning and, after spending the night in drunken celebration, the discovery of this solitary old man in the frozen darkness was very disheartening. It seemed to be such a sad way for someone to welcome in the New Year. Feeling bad for the old Mad Bicycler, we didn't say much for the remainder of the ride.

Then there was the night a friend of mine was on his way up to visit when his headlights caught the old man's eyes, and on Chuck's sworn word, it made them flash a brilliant red. That tale always struck me as being a bit far-fetched, but to this day, both Chuck and his wife Mary, swear that it's true: that the Mad Bicycler has glowing red eyes.

Naturally we would joke about him. We would invent tales connecting him to odd events around the neighborhood that were interesting, if not at all probable. If we heard that the local fire tower windows had been recently smashed out, we would all agree that the Mad Bicycler was to blame. If someone's car battery was stolen, or if a child was lost in the woods for a spell, it was him.

But in our hearts, all of us knew better. He was just a harmless old crackpot doing what he loved to do. He was just something to look for while driving down County Highway 4. Like the habit you have when you travel the same path over and over and over again. You tend to look into people's yards, to see how their garden is doing, or watch them put up a new garage. You check to see how much water is in this section of the river, or make note of the red maples turning color in the early fall. Little things to pass the time.

The Mad Bicycler became just another diversion. Someone to keep an eye out for as your car rolled down the pavement.

Then he was ax murdered. That striking inconsistency is what drew me to writing this tale. It happened out behind his one-room shack in early winter.

Apparently, and most of this information came to me via the local pub, he had just received a $30 check from Social Security when his young nephew, who was very drunk and flat broke at the time, came to borrow some money from him. The old man must have refused to sign his check over because there followed a fight that ended in his nephew taking an ax to the old man out behind the shed. He made off with the $30 check and went on quite a binge. The Mad Bicycler's body laid there for some time before it was discovered.

After that, of course, there was an investigation, the newspaper stories, the radio and television coverage and all the rest. Eventually, the sheriff put two and two together and the nephew was arrested. There followed the trial, the conviction and the life sentence.

But it still doesn't make sense. That all that winter and now, all the seasons that have followed, the Mad Bicycler won't be walking his big blue bike down Highway 4 any longer. That he was brutally slain for thirty dollars. And that somewhere out behind his one-room cabin, his classic, sky-blue-painted bike lies rusting in the rain as I finish this tale.

Not that anyone ever said life makes sense.

Spring, 1969

Epilogue

Way Under Contract is a work of fiction. What has occurred in Florida over the past 50 years is not. In 1950, the population of Florida was 2,771,305. The projected population from the 2000 census is expected to exceed 15,428,000. On average, for every decade during the past 50 years, Florida's population has effectively doubled.

For the wildlife of the Sunshine State, this unprecedented growth has been devastating. Golf courses, suburbs, condominiums, apartment buildings, shopping centers, freeways, office buildings, the immeasurable uprootings of man, all serve to displace animals who once called those pastures, swamps and forests home. They retreat in silence. Some, like the Florida panther and the manatee, retreat to the very brink of extinction. Extinction being the longest silence.

Way Under Contract is not **a** Florida story. It is **the** Florida story. It is the story of section, township and range. The tale of men who see the world, not through the childlike eyes of wonder, but through the eyes of lot and block. The eyes of money. The men who clear the slash pines, burn the saw palmetto and lay the footings for the next exclusive subdivision, complete with lighted tennis courts, Olympic-sized swimming pools and exotic landscaping from every corner of the planet. All this while the native trees and shrubs lie smouldering in the distance, and the gopher tortoises, egrets and indigo snakes try to find a patch of land unscathed by the merciless roar of the bulldozer. Search to find someplace, anyplace to call home.

When you purchased this book, one dollar of the proceeds

went to the Sanibel-Captiva Conservation Foundation. The foundations members are dedicated to the acquisition, restoration and preservation of wildlife habitat. They purchase the land, clear it of the invasive exotics such as Brazilian pepper, and let it be. In effect, they buy the land for the native flora and fauna which can hardly afford to own property in Florida any longer. Purchase it for the herons, river otters and butterflies who don't know what fee simple title is. For the animals who cannot read the fine print.

But it isn't just for the wildlife. It's for us. It's for a future that has William Blake's immortal *"Tiger! Tiger! burning bright"* still in it. It's to ensure for our children that there will always be panthers out there, prowling the primordial hammocks of the Everglades, and that they will be there forever.

It is for them and the generation after them, and for a thousand generations to come. Because if you really want to invest in tomorrow, purchase land, restore it and walk away. That investment is for you, your children and for the creatures, insects and plants who share this glorious Earth with us.

But one dollar is not enough. Nor is money all you can give. If you have time, volunteer. If you have talent, teach. If you have ability, lead. Find an organization nearest you that is dedicated to acquiring and preserving land and get involved. A nature conservancy, a land trust, a conservation foundation that strives to keep that 10-acre swamp from being drained, filled and used for yet another shopping mall. The ceaseless paving of paradise.

Do whatever you can, but please do something. Help to preserve the wondrous beauty of this irreplaceable planet. If you can, make a tax-deductible contribution to the Sanibel-Captiva Conservation Foundation, P.O. Box 839, Sanibel, Florida 33957. Or go to www.indigopress.net and find the link that takes you to a list of conservation groups throughout Florida. You will also find a link to organizations dedicated to saving Florida's endangered sea turtles.

Each of us, working alone, can do little to stop this alarming march of progress. But together we can save an acre here, a hundred acres there and, hopefully over time, a hundred thousand acres and more. The late Dr. Archie Carr, who dedicated his life to turning the tide on the extinction of our sea turtles, summed it up by saying, *"For most of the wild things on Earth the future must depend upon the conscience of mankind."*

We must speak for those whose voice is the song of the mockingbird and the wind rustling the fronds of the cabbage palm. Do it for that child within yourself and the generations of children yet to be. But most importantly, please do it.

Excerpt from ***Way Under Contract***
October, 2000

To Irving Who Vanished

*P*erhaps it was because your father sold soybean bacon to the Japanese. For I still hold a secret disdain toward the marvels of the soybean. Perhaps it was for deeper, more religious motives. But that evening, only moments after the sun had vanished behind the dusty grain elevators of Chicago's south side, you also vanished.

In a way, it was prearranged. Tacit and understood as I handed you my red-and-black anarchist knit cap to keep your head warm and Steven loaned you the ten dollars that you thought you might need if no one in town would cash your check.

It was a Sunday evening and the three of us had worked hard all day on the oreboat anticipating some time on solid land. Steven and I were looking forward to getting drunk in the huge town of Chicago and our cab was on its way to ferry the three of us off into the approaching darkness.

That's when you mentioned something about wanting to see your mother. That was in such perfect character, Irving, wanting to see your mother. So we split up, you with my favorite cap and Steven's ten dollars and me with Steven and an urge to get drunk.

Oh, but there is so much more to say about you. How the people at the union hall laughed at us when we later told them that you failed to return. Or how you had read every Matt Helm book on board within three days of your arrival. Or that you never really fit into the role of an oreboat sailor, with too thick of glasses and a seventh-grade Catholic face. Nor should I forget to point out that you had once attended college for a while to become a chemist. But you aren't a chemist, Irving. No, you are little more than a bit deranged deckhand who vanished one night into the utter void of Chicago. Leaving behind a photo of your high school girlfriend Beth and a rather meaningless IOU.

Untitled, Spring, 1972

Make A Big Splash, Or Group Suicide,
A Novel Group Therapy

*L*et's face it, killing yourself can be a drag. A wet, cloudy day, late afternoon, drizzle falling and melancholia hitting you broadside. You loll around all afternoon, re-reading that "Dear John," letter from your girlfriend, total up your ever-mounting debts, morbidly dwelling on the utter hopelessness of your existence and reach for a pen and paper, writing your farewell note, "To whom it may concern."

From a distance, there's a bizarre humor to it all. A silliness that only a diehard existentialist can appreciate. But for the person about to commit suicide laughter comes hard. Life is a complete bummer, and the worst thing about taking your own life, is that you have to go that final round alone. Suicide is a solo flight, a swan song soliloquy, a one-man show.

Which got me to thinking. Why not include others in this timeless ritual of doing oneself in? What if, instead of a single note, we could write entire volumes of farewells, all linked together by a common theme - self-inflicted death. Then perhaps suicide would be fun. Self destruction would be more like a charter flight to a foreign country. Like a bus trip to Canada, or a macabre kind of group therapy. Much more thrilling that this one-on-one faceoff with our own mortality that is today's fashion of bidding adieu.

Looking further into this "Big Splash" theory, I've come up with a few ideas as to how we could execute these group suicides. Let's take a few minutes to explore each of them more carefully.

1) THE FAMILY CIRCLE. For best results with this particular method of group extinction, we need at least six moderately to severely depressed people, and six hefty .45 revolvers. The participants in the family circle should at least be casually acquainted with each other and dead set on blowing each other's brains out.

It's sometimes a good idea to have a little "rap session" before the actual event to allow the group members to kind of get to know each other a bit before their demise. Learn about each other's likes and dislikes, their hobbies and their hopes for the future, a short-lived future at that.

After an hour of friendly chatting, exchanging recipes, fishing holes, etc., the members of the group all sit in a little circle on the floor and get down to the business at hand. Once comfortably seated, everyone picks up their magnums, loads them with one hollow-point bullet and places the barrel of the pistol directly toward the temple of the person sitting to their immediate right. (Note: If you want to try something different here, you can also be creative and point your guns to the left!).

It's a good idea to have one last little go around, allowing everyone to explain why they can't go on any longer, blah, blah, blah and then comes the final countdown. The entire group, which can be as small as two and as large as imaginable, counts down from ten. Of course timing and determination are of the utmost importance in The Family Circle method of group suicide. If any individual fails to pull the trigger and blow off his companion's head, whilst the companion has dutifully complied with his responsibility, the remaining member is immediately arrested and booked for first-degree murder.

A pleasant way to avoid this unpleasantry is to have everyone sing, *"May the Circle, be unbroken. Bye and bye, Lord, bye and bye,"* just prior to the countdown. Somehow or other, this always seems to assure everyone's mutual annihilation.

2) HANDCUFFS AND BRIDGES. All that we need here are several pairs of handcuffs and a very high cliff or bridge. This method works best with four or five suicides but must have a minimum of two to be effective.

The standard methodology is to have the suicides handcuff

themselves together. Once securely handcuffed together, the keys to the handcuffs are generally thrown off the bridge first, to assure everyone involved of their sincerity. (Note: These keys make wonderful keepsakes if you're lucky enough to find one.)

Once again, the entire group counts down from ten and pushes off. The irony here is that should an individual suicide have a sudden change of heart, the combined weight and momentum of the other jumpers invariably pulls him to his death regardless. Unlike the Family Circle method, this particular technique seldom leaves us any survivors.

3) WAR. As a form of mass suicide, war has proven to be both extremely popular and effective. The particular devices, customs, and justifications for these wars are so ingenious and numerous that I will leave it up to the reader's imagination to recall his particular favorite. I've always been partial to WWI, mostly because no one seems to know why it was ever fought in the first place, but also because of the extensive use of poison gas. Leave it to us to invent something so insidious as poison gas.

The best thing about war is that it's usually so well-disguised amidst political or religious convictions that few of us, if any, see it for what it really is: mutual mass suicide. Another interesting footnote to this method is that we now have the unique ability, thanks to the H-bomb, to handcuff every living thing on the planet together and end it all.

4) EARTH SUICIDE DAY. In conclusion I would like to suggest that we, the people of the earth, either decide to go on living or declare a Universe Wisdom Holiday and commit global suicide. With our ever increasing nuclear stockpiles and doomsday machines, we could very easily arrange such a festive event.

We could somehow tie it in to the real Earth Day, with more of a lemming-like feel to it. This way, we wouldn't have to belabor our slow environmental demise. You know, the cancers, the emphysema, the vast assortment of pollution-related diseases. No, by having an Earth Suicide Day we could go out with a bang.

Humanity could clean the slate of Mother Earth and allow her to begin again the slow, meandering trek of evolution. She could make a fresh start, free of PCBs, hydrocarbons and paint thinner. With all the radiation bouncing around after a good nuclear farewell you can rest assured there would be some interesting mutations helping to kick-start a whole new era of evolution. One without us included, I might add.

Perhaps, just before that final day, we could leave a note on the moon saying, "To Whom it May Concern..." Beside it, we could leave a trunk full of memoirs for some future alien to discover. In it we could place a number of items that would best reflect the highly intelligent if miscreant nature of our culture. Things like a McDonald's cheeseburger, a cheap bottle of red wine (screw top only), a spare tire, some dirty pictures, a deck of cards, well, let's face it, the list is both twisted and endless. Just like this Universe Wisdom column you're reading.

The UMD Statesman, May, 1973

Something Should Be Said About Michael And The Fly

*I*n the late fall of 1969 my friend Michael took a job with the Duluth Mesabi and Iron Range Railroad. After two weeks of local track-gang work he was unexpectedly reassigned and transferred up to the Iron Range. There, some 90 miles from Duluth and 30 miles from anywhere, he was pulled from the track-gang and given his new job. His new assignment was to drive, in a rickety old yellow school bus, a hardy group of old-timers to and from a section of track they were repairing.

You take a job with the railroad and end up being a bus driver, reflected Michael. Such is life. Not that his new job was all that bad. After reluctantly starting that first brisk morning, he found that the bus ran well and it was far less strenuous than working a ten-pound sledge hammer all day.

The only drawback to his new occupation were his living quarters. Most of the old-timers he picked up every morning lived at home amidst the vast scrub forests of northern St. Louis County, but Michael's apartment was back in Duluth. Even if Michael had owned a car, commuting the distances involved was out of the question. Fortunately, the railroad had anticipated the problem.

Upon Michael's arrival, his new boss, a coverall-wearing, snuff-chewing, constantly swearing old codger, solemnly led Michael to his new home. It was like a visit to the local morgue. Michael's new residence was a converted 1903 railroad passenger car. Judging from the cobwebs and disarray inside, it had not been used since 1904. It was a morgue, awaiting a new tenant.

The entire car reeked the unforgettable odor of damp, musty old mattresses. There was a layer of dust a half-inch thick and all manner of garbage and refuse lying about the long, narrow railroad car. No place like home, thought Michael.

His boss, lifting his right hand and pointing with an ancient, rusty finger that resembled a railroad spike, pointed to one of the eight bunks and said, "That one's all yours, son." With that, Michael took his duffel bag, walked over and sat down on the dusty mattress and said, in a very terse tone, "Thanks."

The old codger, ignoring Michael's sarcasm, turned and headed back outside. Without so much as glancing back he added, "See ya in the morning, son."

Michael just sat there, occasionally glancing around the empty car, noting the cobwebs, empty milk cartons, worn-out work boots and boxes of soggy, outdated signal flares, and tried to keep from breaking into tears. Given to outbreaks of unchecked existentialism, he began to wonder about the meaning of it all.

So this is it, he reflected. To wake up at five in the morning in an empty, dilapidated ex-passenger car, heat up some coffee on the electric Pullman range, crawl into your dirty coveralls and head off to pick up a dozen stinking railroad workers for three dollars and change an hour. Not to negate the added satisfaction of his bologna and mustard sandwich for lunch.

Come nightfall, after dropping his busload of even more stinking workers off at their various homes, cars and bars, Michael would return to his lifeless 1903 ex-passenger railroad car. He would park the bus in the same exact spot he had found it in the morning and walk across an empty field to his desolate, empty quarters.

Once inside his glorified boxcar, it was back to the same decaying mattress smells and staring at a railroad car filled with nada. Michael was beginning to question his ability to endure.

Weekends, unfortunately, brought little relief. He didn't have a car to get back to Duluth and the DM&IR Railroad Company naturally refused to allow him the use of their bus. He did find time to read a faded paperback he had found under one of the beds titled,

Hotel of Lust along with a copy of a 1961 Life magazine with the cover torn off. Being a normal, 19-year-old American male, he found his weekend plans somewhat disappointing. And that is putting it very mildly.

At the end of the second full week of this morose routine, it happened. Michael had pulled up his bus on a chilly Friday afternoon, steering it carefully into the exact same tire ruts he had driven it out of that morning, turned the lumbering machine off, and walked across the dead leaves and brown grass into his home away from home. His morgue.

He plopped down on the same corner of his bed, dreading the thought of the upcoming long weekend, and tried to keep from weeping. That's when he heard it. It was a distinct, loud, "Buzzzz." It was late October and Michael couldn't believe that a fly could possibly have survived this late into the season. There had already been several heavy frosts and the entire insect world had assuredly hunkered down for the winter by now.

But there it was again, "Buzzzz." Was it really a fly? A leftover pest from the beautiful green of summer. But where was this remnant of warmer, happier times? Michael began a silent, sonar style search for this winged insect.

Suddenly not a sound was heard. But he has to be here somewhere, thought Michael. I know I just heard him. He grabbed the Life magazine, rolling it up in anticipation of the kill, and listened even more intently. That's when it hit him.

Why kill it? He had another long, empty weekend ahead of him and, at this point, even a bug could provide him some welcome companionship. Maybe he could befriend it? It would be nice to have another living thing around, even if it was a lowly fly.

With those thoughts in mind, Michael began calling for him. He clenched his teeth together, and making a decisive "B" sound, made a long, somewhat amateurish, "Buzzzz." Only it sounded more like "Buzzzschh." No matter. Within a few minutes the fly re-sponded, no doubt looking for his own insect companionship.

Michael heard the response and was elated. "Buzzzz." "Buzzzschh." "Buzzzz." "Buzzzschh." They communicated back and forth until Michael stood next to the window pane where his new-found friend was trying hopelessly to get out. Michael looked down and felt sorry for the fly. He was a big fly, bright blue with dark hairy legs and strong, powerful wings. Great, thought a forlorn railroad worker, I've finally found a friend. A gift from God.

The next Monday morning came with considerable improvement. Michael had spent the entire weekend with his fly and the time had passed a thousand times faster than it had the two prior weekends. He had even named him. The fly's new name was Ludwig. Michael and Ludwig had spent the last 48 hours together in perfect harmony. Michael had explained why he needed this particular job, how much he missed his ex-girlfriend, Sally, and on and on like two old friends who hadn't talked in a decade. Ludwig's responses were limited to "Buzzzz's" of both long and short duration.

When the sun rose above the frozen earth of late October that following Monday, Michael looked over at Ludwig, still stuck on the same window sill, and shouted, "It's a wonderful day to be alive, Ludwig." Ludwig agreed, saying simply, "Buzzzz."

Their conversation continued up until the time that Michael was to head off to work. Giving his usual, what have I forgotten this morning look over his musty home, he noticed for the very first time all the tiny holes and cracks throughout the old passenger car. No way, he quickly surmised. If I leave without taking care of all of these openings, Ludwig might escape. God, I'd really miss him.

He spent the next ten minutes hurriedly patching and stuffing all the holes in the railraod car with pages from *Hotel of Lust,* which wasn't a bad read the first time, but by the sixth reading it had grown dull and pointless. Even the poorly contrived sex scenes had lost their luster.

Returning home from work that evening was delightful. Michael rolled the old school bus in, intentionally neglecting to park it in the same ruts, and quickly hiked back inside of his railroad car to see how things were with Ludwig. They were great. Upon opening the door, the very first thing that Michael heard was the familiar sound of Ludwig's voice. "Buzzzz." Ludwig, quite naturally, was back at his favorite window pane, trying in vain to fly through the quarter-inch-thick plate glass to his freedom beyond.

"Silly fly," said Michael. "It's damn cold out there. If you were to make it out, you wouldn't last a day." To calm him down, Michael went over to his small fridge, took out a tiny piece of bologna and placed it on the window sill beneath the hovering fly. Smelling the food, Ludwig quickly stopped his vain attempts at fleeing, and settled down on the lunch meat. It was delicious. Had he been able to, Ludwig would have thanked his new friend Michael for being so thoughtful.

For the next few days things kept getting better for both Michael and the fly. Ludwig eventually gave up trying to escape the warm passenger car, and Michael soon found the fly's company very agreeable. For long hours before falling asleep Michael would just lie there in his bunk and relate long, colorful stories about his life. He would talk to Ludwig about missing his high school sweetheart, Sally Swenson, and how he didn't understand why she had wanted to break up. He would talk to Ludwig about his dad, the divorce, and how he didn't really understand why that had to happen either.

He told Ludwig everything. Why he had taken this particular job with the railroad. Why he needed the money to continue on with college and what his plans were after graduation. He talked about missing his buddies back in Duluth and how he was going to party like mad once this repair was completed in late November and he was laid off for the winter. Ludwig listened attentively, if not for any other reason than Michael's voice being the only sound besides the wind within 20 miles.

Everything was going well. The old railroad workers, all of whom Michael disliked, were becoming friendlier. The transmission in the old, yellow school bus shifted better and the dry, lifeless autumn didn't seem quite as forsaken as it once had. Indeed Ludwig, a big blue fly, was a welcome pal and a decent insect.

That following Friday, a week after their chance meeting, Michael woke up with a profound sense of duty. Rolling up the coverless 1961 Life magazine, Michael laid back down on his bunk and listened. "Buzzzz." There, on the table, landed Ludwig. Michael rose, and headed toward the unwary insect silently. Within a few steps, Michael stood there, towering above the lowly pest. The rolled-up Life magazine, the fly, the arm drawing back, the loud, sudden smack on the table. The fly was gone.

That night, after parking the bus, Michael quit work without notice and hitch-hiked home. A few months later, at college, I knew immediately that something should be said about Michael and the fly.

There Is Much To Find Sorrow In

*I*have no doubt that the world rests upon the bloody shoulders of the human endeavor. Our grand parade of weaponry from rocks to sticks, from fire to hydrogen appears to never end. It is as if we are forever renewing ourselves in the technology of our own displacement. Our chosen alienation from the Eden that has always surrounded us.

Let the record speak for itself. Drag out the chronicles, the sordid histories, the maimed and the buried and let them all speak their hideous testimony to the saga that has been our brief but lurid walk through time. Call up the extinct as expert witnesses. Let them document the excesses we have wrought upon them. Bring in both the cavalry and the Calvary of our answer to innocence. The Little Big Horn and the Crucifix of it all.

Yes, my dear reader, there is much to find sorrow in. There is sadness in every page of that transcript, being read aloud to this jury of Deities for the second time. Not that they will listen to it in an effort to change their verdict. No, they are simply astonished at the magnitude of the crime. They want it repeated, as though by hearing it aloud one last time they might make it vanish. As if pleading to the courtroom, "Please, just say it isn't so."

But it is so. It is the way we are, both in the annals of human history and in our individual lives. Killing friendships, wasting time, squandering love and forgiving no one. Encircled in this ritual of birth and death without taking the time to simply sit down, breathing in and out slowly, and listening. Listening to the rhythm of our own heartbeats, the symmetry of our own existence, laid before us in this chorus of pleasure and pain. Mindfulness at its finest.

Because there is no way to atone for the sins of the world. Sorrow, sadness, even depression can take you under their shadowy wing, but it will not change one sentence on the pages upon pages of our tarnished past. We have sinned, we are sinning, and we will sin again. That is the way it is with us, and all the prayers and wailing in the universe will not erase a single black mark. Trying to do so is folly.

That being self evident, where do we turn for reprieve? We turn to the God within. We turn to our own angel and ask that we be judged, not by the crimes committed by our fellow man, but by our own actions. That every day, every moment is a new unwritten text where we have both the right and the ability to make amends for that long, forbidden past that has delivered us here. That there is no time to change that past, but infinite time to change the future. Infinite and possible.

That the human spirit can, and will lift itself up from its own mire. That individually it will survive and forgive itself. That we will each be free of this grim chronology and that we will not let the future go there again.

That there will never be a furnace built again that resembles the ovens of Auschwitz. That the war between the states is over, and we are not North and South anymore than we are East and West. That the Inquisition and the Crusades were madness personified, and that we should never again let our theologies come between the commonality of the family of man. If there are Gods, and I pray that there are, I know that they would never wish this on us; that we would kill each other in their names. The only gods I can think of that would do such a thing answer to Lucifer.

Because there is so much in the world to be thankful for. There is this chance to share and to give. There is the chance to be there for people, to help them get back up on their feet. To care. There is the sweet, invisible air that we breathe and bask in. There is the brilliant sunlight and there is the glorious rainlight. There is the wash of color that is everything, the song of the wind, even in its stillness. There is someone whom you love and, even should they never love you in return, how much better the person you are for loving them. There are your parents, your family, your friends and your self. Alive and able to partake of making tomorrow better. More understanding. More giving.

Sorrow and sadness have their places, as do fear and apprehension. But they need not have a place in our lives today.

Go then. And every moment of every waking hour, ask yourself this simple question: How does it feel to be alive?

It feels wonderful.

Poetry
(1969-2001)

Author's Notes

I have always felt that poetry is the soul of all great writers. This is despite the fact that many writers never draft a single line of verse. For them, I suspect, the poetry remains within. For writing poetry is a joy. It is like visiting a world of language freed from the confines of syntax and grammar. At its best, it is spontaneous combustion. The transmutation of heart and soul to pen and paper.

Over the years I have never strayed far from my copy of Walt Whitman's *Leaves of Grass*. My brother, Steven, gave it to me in college, and the binding now has all but disintegrated. Ginsberg, Ferlinghetti, Emily Dickinson and the writings of an obscure beat poet, Kenneth Patchen, have all hung with me over the years like a gang of metaphorical punks on the joy ride of verse.

Many of the poems included are taken from *Untitled*, published in 1972. Most of the 100 pages consisted of poetry. The other collections you will see noted: *Birds of Paradise* (1973), *Convolutions* (1974), *Of the Blue Door* (1975), *Closetbeard* (1976), *Stationary* (1977) and *My Performance* (1978), were never published. At the end of each year I would compile my scribbling, select a precious few, then meticulously rework them and bind them into dimestore folders, tucking them away for another time. That time is now.

A few of the poems included have been published, some in the *Islander* and *Island Reporter*, a few in *The Sanibel-Captiva Review*. A small group of dedicated writing enthusiasts here on Sanibel publish the *Review* annually. It is a worthwhile read.

I have always tried to make my poems accessible. In recent years, poetry has fallen on hard times. In an electronic world overwhelmed with video and telecommunications, poetry seems about as misplaced as does the manatee. Some of you will want to skip this section entirely. I hope you don't. One of these poems will speak to you clearer than anything else possibly could. Enjoy the journey.

Charles Sobczak
August, 2001

let the poem be

let the poem be unto its own.
don't handle it
carelessly or want trifling explanations from it.
let the poem be a tennis shoe,
or a radio,
or a fat man on roller skates.
and don't go pushing it,
or wanting it to tell you
any well-kept secrets.
just let it be,
and don't be goofing around with it.
let it occur just as naturally as
you have occurred.
don't raise your voice to it
or try to change it after it has decided
its course.
let the poem be itself
like its own heartbeat.
nothing to bend
or tie things unto but to
leave alone.
let the poem be a flower,
or a mountain range,
or a rusty car rolling down eighth street,
with the driver and his girlfriend
in the backseat
making out.

Untitled, Spring, 1969

When Roses Fall

Petal by petal they empty into air.
Vanish like time does, without a trace.
Their brilliant red, red luster fades,
They fall. They lose their tender grace.

For all in changing does the circle close.
Once born, once severed from the stem.
The bloom retreats in silent beauty 'til,
That silent beauty has its mournful end.

Our careful hands in vain, do what they will.
Choose the slender vase, the water fresh.
Can but forestall their sad demise,
To watch the petals fall. Then lay to rest.

Where beauty stood, with every passing glance,
Is now a memory of empty stem and thorn.
It is the fate of beauty, to bloom and fall,
Just as it is who hears the cry of being born.

When roses fall, as soon these roses shall,
Their scarlet brilliance stolen by the hour,
Think not young, nor old, nor in a sadness dwell,
It is the perfect tale of every gentle flower.

July, 1995

She is Ocean

She is ocean.
He is land.
Smooth.
Jagged.

She changes with the wind.
Temperamental, moody and elusive.
He remains firm.
Predictable, self-assured.

She is water. Pure azure.
Liquid and flowing, not unlike her tears.
He is not.
He is dark and stalwart. The color of rocks.

She is eternal.
A soft rhythm that goes on forever, like the tides.
He is finite.
Moving in thick chunks of time.

She is graceful.
Watercolors in moonlight, songs of the night wind.
He is rough.
Broad daylight appeals to him.

They meet at the shoreline of love.
It is a complicated place, full of beaches, cliffs
And ceaseless waves.
Some whispering.
Some raging.   *(continued)*

Their relationship is never easy.
They need each other to complete the circle.
They do not need each other to be free.

Children are born.
Some wander out to sea and become women.
Some head inland to make things.
Things that grind.

These are things that will never change.
She is ocean.
He is land.

1996

War

My father drunken, sadly once
      began about the war.
Some small island off of New Zealand
      where a buddy left an arm,
Like a forgotten piece of luggage.
      But my father's staggering
memory

Couldn't quite remember its name.
      I told him that we could look it up,
but he just kept wondering why
      he'd forgotten.
Until he started crying and suddenly ending
      about
the war.

Untitled, Fall, 1970

Not More Than This

We invent our prisons.
Patiently placing brick upon brick,
Mortar, stone and sand until we are perfectly encased.
We even have cell mates with whom we go out to dinner.
Take on boat rides,
Share cocktails and play cards.
To pass the time I guess.
Make it seem less like
Incarceration.

This is our life for the most of us.
And, in many ways, it is the best we can expect.
The individual cells are clean, comfortable.
The guards are all self imposed,
Old friends mostly, with some family members
Stationed in particularly vulnerable areas.

Sure, there are times we would like to escape, but
There would be those unnerving cries of alarm,
The sirens and the searchlights
Followed by a pack of barking dogs.
Dogs pulling on strained leashes.
Pulling hard.

And then there would be the talk.
Oh the talk!
How it would reverberate
Down along those cellblocks.
First to those closest to the escapee,
Then beyond, making the rounds of that prison
Faster than a Pentium processor.   (continued)

By then you would be far, far away.
Lying in some mosquito-infested swamp,
With the dogs clamoring in the distance and that
Steve McQueen look in your eyes.
Like a Saturday afternoon matinee,
Only real.

And in no time at all you would start to miss the joint.
With its night lights and fresh baked bread.
You would start to miss the cable TV,
With 50-plus channels
All showing the same program.

And you would miss the security of it all.
The safety.
By daybreak, you would be ready to turn yourself in again.
Like you did the last time and the time before that.

And you would go back to your ten-by-ten cell,
Overly apologetic and more than humbled.
They would all welcome you back, smiling,
Saying they sort of understand.
We invent our prisons, and in turn,
They invent us.

July, 1995

A Conversation Between Two Snow Shovels

This morning the snow arrived here
Like a tourist planning to stay the winter.
Cars were soon becoming disgusted with it.
School kids were rolling in it like
Piglets in white mud.

By noon it looked as though the chances
Of its melting were slight.
I took up my aluminum shovel as a soldier would
His rifle and marched to my sidewalk to do battle.
But the snow was light and it was a peaceful skirmish.

Across the street my neighbor
Was also shoveling off his sidewalk.
His shovel would go scraaaaaaape.
Then my shovel would go scraaaaaaape.
Our shovels talked like this for half an hour.

It was a casual meeting between two old friends
Who hadn't seen each other since last spring.
They chatted some about old times,
recalling wet, heavy snows and brittle cold.
They asked about the broom and ice pick
while removing the snow from the concrete pathway
like one would a slightly used white carpet.

I finished before my neighbor and
rather rudely brought their
conversation to an end.

November, 1971

3 american poems

1.
Want
money.
Want split level home
with T-bone dinners.
Want
fast car with
four fat tires.
Want to
screw til dawn
with a beautiful movie star.
Want
lots of money &
a pretty wife built
in Chicago by a
smooth machine.
Want peace with a
war built economy.
Want good health
and color television.
Want a camper truck
with a four wheeler
and want
what they say
I'll...

2.
Take
what I can get.
Take my time.
Take a raise.
Take down this
important message.
Take a chance.
Take a vacation.
Take four of these daily.
Take a ride.
Take a turn at the
ring toss, sucker.
It's your life because you...

3.
Need
a quick exit.
Need a rock soup.
A thatched hut.
Need to be lost
in your jungles
without cell phones
or elevators
or willing ambulances.
Need nakedness
with pure sunlight
& no lotions.
But stripped to the
teeth of necessity.
Like needing
each other without the
polished
nothingness stuck between.

Untitled, 1973

Anne

(I)

Such loss is lent to Pentecost,
My tongues have fled to thee.
Whose beauty late, has touched this skin,
That soil and stone have callused so,
And set the captive free.
But the wounded least forget the hunt,
When love has drawn the bow.
So mark my pain, with scarce complaint.
For fear the kill, with passing would,
In habit, spend this flame.

(II)

The moon, my love, is liquid,
An enchanting, sweet liqueur,
Distilled of youthful passions,
To thee, to us I pour.
I pour, my love, at midnight,
In goblets spun of glass.
As fragile as this dream I have
Of holding you at last.
Of finding you beside me,
Your touch, the warmest flame,
Would make a raging fire seem ice
And put the sun to shame.
The moon, my love, is restless.
She beckons me, *be quick!*
To find you at this moonlit hour
And offer you this gift.

My Performance Collection, 1978

I Carve Words

See language as forest.
Follow me deeper and deeper into this metaphor.
See my insights as hardy loggers, lumberjacks if you wish.
Men with big, burly beards and those L.L. Bean flannel shirts.
See them choosing the right tree to fell,
The one yielding the best lumber,
The stalwart pine bearing the best imagery I can work with.

See the huge fallen tree as the draft.
Too many misleading branches attached,
The bark thick and enigmatic.
The shape all wrong.
Somewhere deep within it lies
A hint of the poem to come.

See the planed-off logs as a mere beginning.
Holding promise, but still unfinished.
Dried and roughed-out lumber
Remaining to be whittled down by hand.
Then sanded and re-sanded until this poem stands alone.
Hour upon hour of careful, patient effort.

And from that lofty first idea,
That crashed with such fury in the depth of the
Ancient forest,
I hand you this singular poem.
It is the size of the small wooden knight
In this chess set I am carving.
A chess set I know may never be played.
But that does not deter me.
I carve words.

1995

Love is a Mist

Love is a mist.
Hanging in the evening air suspended upon itself.
Needing only a moon to add proportion.
That, and two hearts to blend.

It rinses the terrible to tender.
The gravel to joy.
Its sweetness devours us as we stir
Together.
Walking slowly into it,
Never wanting to be found again.

Winter, 1999

Yellow Flowers, Gray Rain

They do not reach
yet they have obtained.
Perhaps the rain
does not fall with any intention
of contrast.
Perhaps the rain falls
because it knows nothing of the perfect.
And perhaps the flowers,
although blind of their own brilliance unfold
the other mystery of
these yellow flowers, gray rain.
They do not strive,
yet they have obtained.

Birds of Paradise Collection, 1974

The Sage's Staff

Everyone has a right,
a God-given right ironically,
to their own explanation.

Some try science.
You know the stuff: cause and effect,
action, reaction.
The laws of motion, gravity and
relativity all interacting in some
Einsteinian soup of logic.
Humorous in a sort of rubber-ducky
kind of way. A make-it-up as we go along kind of thing.
And why not?
Even God's good for a laugh now and then.

Others try religion.
Granted, it's a little bit better approach.
But sooner or later, they've always got the
"We're holier than thou" thing going.
Not much holier mind you.
Just enough
To put someone else's feet to the coals.
A twisted litmus test for Jesus, or Allah, or Shiva
If you are leaning in that direction.
In any case, it ends up looking a lot like torture,
and not religion. Though they've tended to
criss-cross each other's turf over the ages.

Then there are the quarks of
our collective consciousness;   (continued)

The nihilists, existentialists, atheists, and
an array of other, randomly assorted "ists."
Their peculiar, idiosyncratic slants elude
even those who spend their lifetime

writing dissertations on them.
Sub-particles in this museum of pictographs.
Sparky and fun to talk about at parties.

But what about that other guy.
You know, the one who likes to stand out
under an ocean of stars
with his family safe and sleeping in their
home upon a vast and endless plain.
His heart so overflowing with wonder
that nothing in this petri-dish of language
can define it.

The humble man who gets up each morning
to work the soil until the sun sets.
Then rests.
Who does not judge, or feel the need to
put the magnifying glass of reason or religion
to the power and the glory that is life.
Who fills his bowl with
only enough for himself and his family.
Who lives, loves and dies in
breathtaking obscurity like
pollen in the winds of time.

(continued)

But therein lie both the answer and the paradox.
In the Sage's staff and
the music of Mozart. Our urge to keep asking why?
When the better
approach has always been
why not?

Summer, 2000

Isabel, the Sweet Moose of My Love

i see your face, all o'er the place,
       in every nook and cranny.
i love ya so, you'll never know,
       ya make me feel so zany.

i drive my car, and never sleep,
       just thinkin' of her kisses.
i quit my job, and never eat,
       just waitin' for me missus.

chorus: oh moose of love, come home to me,
            come sit upon my shoulder.
      i'd lose in chess, or climb a tree,
         if only i could hold her.

there's peanuts in this life i lead,
       and popcorn in my sorrow.
but I'd skin a fish, or rent a horse,
       if she'd return tomorrow.

oh love is cruel, like eating gruel
       or swimming in a sandbox.
my heart is vacant, i grow impatient,
       for her i'd catch the smallpox.

chorus: oh moose of love, come home to me,
            come sit upon my shoulder.
      i'd lose in chess, or climb a tree,
         if only i could hold her.

(continued)

so sweet moose dear, just cuddle near,
　　your snout about my arms.
for love went weird, when you appeared,
　　i's dazzled by your charms.

and now i'm empty, a ship at sea,
　　a golf ball down the sewer.
explain i can't, though crave and rant,
　　if only you had knew her.

chorus: oh moose of love, come home to me,
　　　come sit upon my shoulder.
　　i'd lose in chess, or climb a tree,
　　　if only i could hold her.

but now she's gone, a blank lagoon,
　　a wing devoid of feathers.
she's taken off, back to the swamp,
　　and left me lost as leather.

January, 1971

i am my own habit

The puppet's cheap teeth rattle.
This voice,
this very whisper, betrays
the stage he stands upon.
And though his is the string he has
his hands upon,
his fingerbones are brittle.
>He is himself
>a bit too well.
The puppet chances little.

So late he sleeps
and avoids his shadow.
For motions memorized are safer far
than letting my
>cheap teeth rattle.

Convolutions Collection, 1974

Beside the Long Highway

Before the phone rang that afternoon in October,
Before the news of the tragedy, the anger and the tears,
They were there.
Pushed into the ground by saddened hands
Beside that long, long Highway.

Along the empty road that leads to Cabo San Lucas
I saw dozens of them.
Wooden Crosses marking where the truck
Full of farm workers failed to make the turn.
Where the accident occurred.
Or the year after that, on the Alcan Highway in the Yukon,
Where the Winnebago flipped and the couple
From Ohio were lost.
The plastic flowers fading in the tundra's endless sunlight.
Dust collecting across the thick wooden
Shoulders of the two crosses alongside the winding road.

Before that terrible phone call three years ago
They were only crosses beside the Highway.
Places where someone else's loved ones had died,
Unconnected and harmless,
Like the sound of thunder in the distance.

But last summer changed all of that.
As I passed Pine City and drew toward
The long valley formed by the Kettle River,
My hands grew tight and sweaty against the steering wheel.
My heart raced helplessly.

(continued)

Your fiancé, Jerry, had placed it there.
Two years before in a ceaseless rain
That fell silently on a forest stripped
Of its color in late October.
A forest preparing for the death of winter.

Your nephew, John, had made it for Jerry.
He was always good with his hands.
Choosing the oak boards, skillfully joining the two planks.
Rounding the edges with the router.
Crying to himself while finishing it.
Remembering you.
His tears falling on the sawdust.

Your Uncle Bob drove Jerry back to the place
Along Interstate 35-W where your car
Left the highway, sliding down the inside bank
For a hundred feet before rolling.
Landing right side up with you no longer in the car.
The place along the highway where you
Took your last breath while
Blue lights flashed and stern Highway Patrol
Officers lit flares and slowed traffic.
While onlookers, strangers
Strained to see what had happened.

That place where the ambulance crew tried to bring you back.
But you were too broken to bring back, Peg.
Just too broken.
Lying still and lifeless beside the bulrushes
That rustled in the light autumn winds,
Still damp from the rain.   (continued)

So as tears welled in my eyes and
My car pulled up over that last knoll before
The nondescript freeway bridge that crosses the Kettle River
I looked for your cross.
The cross beside the long Highway.

The cross the bears that name of my little sister, Peggy.
The cross that Jerry and my older sister Barb takes care of.
By that place where Peggy's smile was stolen from us.
Where the wrecker had taken the car
An hour after the ambulance had taken her body.

As tears fell from my eyes, and I heard
The clicking of the expansion joints as my Volvo crossed
The Kettle, heading north toward Duluth,
I realized for the very first time what those crosses mean.
I knew that I would never see them the same.

Because those crosses tell stories.
Places where families were devastated.
Children gone. Fathers, mothers and sadness unknown.
Places where hearts are re-broken with every passing.
Small wooden crosses beside the long Highway.

The flowers will fade,
The crosses will become weathered and crooked over time.
But in my heart her cross will never falter,
Her flowers shall not perish, even when covered by the
Deepest snows of winter.
In my heart I will preserve her wooden cross forever.
Until that day when my cross finds its own place somewhere
Beside that same long Highway.

Fall, 1997

All the Little Giants

They came as I remembered them, with eyes of shoelace brown.
And never once did they repeat that soft and frightened sound.
The emblems that appeared as well, arranged like magnets in a row
Were seeking their polarity, by asking where to go?

And all the little giants, whose names elude my guess,
Were carving their initials on my favorite wooden desk.
I did not reprimand them then, and I would not do so still.
For when my raspy breath exhales, you'll find them in my will.

And I will give them all I had; my joy, my time, my singing.
With every photo left so still, in this album I'm creating.
Then all the little giants will no longer little be,
But taking pictures of the next, small tick of history.

1995

Insignificantly Worse

They announced it in the fall.
Those strange chaps in white smocks and thick glasses.
Beady-eyed men with algebraic calculations scattered
Amidst their thoughts.
They had just received their information
First hand from the new, improved Hubble telescope.
The telescope that had just been refitted
With its very own pair of thick glasses.
The telescope was now just one of the guys.
Scientist guys.

None of them gave the discovery any personal reflection.
To them it was just another calculation to enjoy.
A quantitative chocolate malt to savor while their
Logarithmic minds slowly sucked it down.
Delicious and exciting at once.
They were going to leave the emotional reaction to me.

It hit me like a comet in the solar plexus.
Like a hematite meteor to the heart.
I became instantly depressed.
The Hubble telescope had just discovered 50 billion new galaxies!
Not 50,
Not even 50 million, which really would have awed me,
But 50 billion brand new, heretofore unknown galaxies.

Bear in mind that none of these were little,
Compact-sized galaxies either.
They were all the big, full-sized ones, oblong or circular,
Spinning eternally in the dark, infinite desolation of space.

(continued)

Most of them with the
Absurdly huge dimensions as our own Milky Way,
Which, by the way, has about 100 billion stars in it.
Some of them were even 100,000 light years larger,
As if at that point it really makes a difference.

The evening after they found this new gigabunch of galaxies
I wandered out into the night sky and glanced up.
The billions upon billions of stars made me feel
Ever so insignificant.
Now, after reading about this latest discovery,
I felt insignificantly worse.

1996

hand me arabian roses

hand me
> extension cords to sapphire,
> blissful luxury of rain.

hand me allegory.
> dressed in dimestore cotton,
> attending the wake of regret.

hand me
> all the details of optics,
> the thinnest card deck possible.

hand me
> arabian roses,
> lashed tautly to ships at sea.
> forgiving no one, nor
> > ever forgiven.

The Blue Door Collection, 1975

How Thin the Line

Like a ballet performed upon a stage of razor blades.
Like the song of a mute,
A song whose melody leaps high above the
Range of human hearing, or runs
Deeper than a chorus of suffering thunderstorms.
How thin the line.

Like an overdose of narcotics.
Like a rushing bull,
Whose matador has left the ring
Leaving only a trail of red, red roses
Leading to the distant edge of time.
How thin the line.

Like the bitter taste of poison.
Like a mountain beneath the sea,
A towering enigma in a dark blue world,
Where ascending and descending both return
Into the crushing depths of life itself.
How thin the line.

Like the prose of a fallen angel.
Like the prejudice of sanity.
A script without characters
Filled with profanities still unspoken.
A memo to saints unborn.
How thin the line.

(continued)

Like this palace of mirrors and dreams.
Like a wind of rage blowing
Within a vortex as yet unnamed.
This place of midnights caught
Between my madness and my genius,
How thin the line.

Winter, 2000

Hunger

The cat was in us then.
The fang and claw of youth.
The roar of inexperience.

And such hunger it was.
Wheeling up and down that tight neon strip.
Our cars leaving their trail
of burnt rubber.
Our shirts the smell of six packs.

Everything was pure appetite.
Pouring into those greasy chains,
Circling, circling, circling.
Then pouring back out again,
Into that asphalt black night,
As wild as sirens.

More and more hunger suspended across
That endless strip.
That fiberglass world of teenage
Short order plans
And their promised-land weekends.

And although the years have burned away
I still feel that hunger as I pass
Through those electric
Stretches of street.
Though my hunger has grown much deeper,
While their promises have grown stale.

Stationary Collection, 1977

Lady After the Bars Close

She has those sliding glass doors for eyes.
  A patio with white,
  delicately twisted iron chairs
  lies a few steps further.

She beckons you to sit down for a while and visit.
  She mixes you a drink
  and places it gently on the small wrought iron table.
  The table is rusted here and there.

She tells you that it gets hard sometimes, keeping up
a place like this without a man around the house.
  You are on your second drink
  by now.
  You notice that the lawn has not been mowed.

An hour or so has passed.
Your conversation has wandered from
words to zippers.
  Both of you give it everything that you have left.
  Over-spending yourselves in this
  newfound gift shop of pleasure.

You fall asleep.
When you awake beside her in the morning
you feel exiled.
  You look into her blue eyes and see that
  the patio doors are shut.
  She doesn't feel like getting out of bed.
You leave.

        Winter, 1976

There was madness...

Michael, the stars are out.
Steven and I stumble about below them
      arguing
over the course of Eridanus, or wondering
      about the friendship of Castor and Pollux.

Michael, it's a perfect December sky above us.
Clear, endless.
      But once,
a few lost years ago, it was a September sky,
      and on that night as well, the stars were out.

Under that September sky
we climbed the granite hills overlooking our city.
There were no constellations in those heavens.
      I saw no river where Phaethon fell,
no myths, no dragons.

For Michael, there was madness that September,
and the stars,
      like the city below us,
were arranged in pure electric lunacy.
      Either vista could
have been a dim, black mirror.

All of us laughing, high as the
      beat poets we worshiped.
Smiling,
as you unfolded a ragged trombone case.
Pausing,
while I tried the nervous clarinet.   *(continued)*

Waiting...
a few words, a cigarette. Waiting...

Then suddenly, like a wind able to sing,
we would turn night's mute breeze
          into a chorus of
dissident angels.

For that September we ascended
          neither too close to heaven,
          nor too far above that city below us.
We ascended
just to the granite where Robert
          was smacking stones to keep even
our screaming measures.
We rose only to the stony hilltops
          where Daniel paced in utter silence.
Where Thomas first felt the rippling
          skin of the saxophone.

We climbed to the heights of discord where
I twisted the tone of the clarinet
          into the voice of an old man
Begging for another chance.

Michael, we climbed to the hills of your horn,
          bellowing out like a frightened saint,
suspended between these dark, mirrored visions.

We flew on wings of a musical madness.
Our lunatic chords curling like flames
          to the lovers parked below us.
Our infant music reaching its tiny hand out
          to the stars above.   (continued)

Michael, years later and December now,
and as Steven and I were gazing up at the
      starry chaos the shepherds once must have known,
the infant's fingers touched Lyra,
      and for a moment this memory sang.

December, 1972

November Portrait

There is no fat in the slanted light of the morning sun.
It is lean and true.
He nods to its raw beauty
as he walks in a hunter's silence across
the frosted lawn.

He is like that: austere.
He is forged of a primal iron,
cast long before the invention of words.

Through his eyes the world looks good today.
The air is sharp and clean,
Blowing calmly from the north.
The autumn leaves are brilliant, still clinging
To the surrounding poplar and mountain ash.
The first heavy frost lies thick upon the grass,
Though the rising sun will melt it off before noon.

In his hand he carries a chain saw.
It is razor sharp.
He cleaned it, adjusted it, and sharpened it
last night after finishing up.
He will do the same tonight.

He is proud of the fact that his saw always
starts on the first pull,
he reflects as he
leans over and wedges it carefully between
the spare tire and the wall of his pickup.
He bought a good saw
and he takes good care of it.   (continued)

He puts the key in the ignition and slams
the heavy door shut.
The truck starts quickly.

He hesitates
before pulling away.
Debating with himself over whether
or not to bring along his dog this morning.
It is a brief, but sincere debate.
The dog can be bothersome while cutting
but he enjoys his company.

He whistles for him.
As the jet black lab, tail wagging, leaps into the
bed of the pickup, he backs out, puts
his truck into third and heads toward
the north forty where they are pulping,
the exhaust of his pickup hanging long and thick
in the cool autumn air.

Fall, 1976

Bigger

Bigger than this.
Bigger than the gigantic neutron
Is to the tiny quark.
Bigger than a best seller.
A best seller that was made into a motion picture
That won seven Academy Awards,
Including Best Picture!
Bigger than money.

Bigger than all of it.
Bigger than the sum of all the parts;
The cosmos, the dark holes, the quasars and
All the awkward telescopes that find them.
Bigger than Everest.
Bigger than the Pacific.
Bigger than law.

Bigger than imagination.
Bigger than hope, or faith, or the
Immense vanity of explanation.
Bigger than any documentation.
Bigger than the redwoods,
And the endless forests they belong to.
Bigger than Tokyo.

Bigger than proof.
Bigger than WWII, and nowhere near as heartless.
Even bigger than religion,
Or prayer, or meditation for that matter.
Bigger than the discovery of penicillin.
Bigger than Jupiter.
Even bigger than the
Hoola hoop craze.

Bigger than reason.
Bigger than time.
Bigger than patience, syntax and
The realm of possibility.
Bigger than Texas.
Way, way bigger than Texas.

Bigger than suffering.
Bigger than delusion, fear
And adversity.
Bigger than the Super Bowl
Between two undefeated teams
On a cold, blustery day in late
January with nothing else worth watching.

Bigger than everything
But love.

July, 1998

Van Gogh's Ear

It happened to me about a week ago.
I was at a party, or it might have been a bar.
It's difficult to get the details straight,
At least, since I still have it.

A complete stranger came up to me and put it in my hand.
It felt cold.
Somehow, I knew immediately what it was,
And at first the very thought of it made me nauseated.

I still have it.
Although I took it out of my pocket a few days ago.
It was starting to give off a peculiar odor.
So now I keep it in a jar next to my computer.

The guy who gave it to me said that it nearly ruined his life.
I can certainly understand why.
It isn't exactly something you go telling your wife about,
Or even your closest friends for that matter.

It's been handed down this way for over a hundred years now.
At parties, social events and, on occasion, by private arrangement.

No one knows exactly why he cut it off.
Some say for love, others say he did it out of passion.

It bothers me to look at it, but it compels me nonetheless.
It certainly can give you mixed emotions.

(continued)

I try to put a positive spin on it, thinking that
At least I realize that I have emotions again.
That in itself is an improvement.

I haven't exactly decided what to do with it.
Perhaps I should mail it, return receipt requested,
directly to you.
Then you can discover for yourself what it does to that
Complacent little
Subcompact world you've been living in.

In fact, look for it in tomorrow's post.

October, 1996

The Way of the World

Old men dine on the flesh of youth -
In the banquet halls of opulence,
In the rookeries of power,
In the war rooms of the world -
Young fools are devoured and lost.

And never a hand is raised to halt this ritual
By those who might dare.
By those whose dissenting voice might endanger their
Inheritance of position and place,
Their portion of the raw feast.

For this is the Way of the World.
It is neither path nor promise nor
An unseen God's ambiguous design.
It is a dark shadow over those who starve
And an overwhelming sunlight above those
Who own the sun.

For as there is laughter in the Great Hall,
There is hunger in the streets below.
As there is contentment on the faces of the elite,
There is yearning on those faces born of a
Lesser legacy.

For callous and cunning is the Way of the World.
Consuming all in its sublime progress and then,
Seeing that what was green and lush
Is now ravaged and ruined,
Does vainly move on.

1977-92

Popular Madness

McGuire snapped that bat and the ball rocketed
Over the right field fence along with a million eyeballs.
For ten minutes in America everything was safe.
Baseball was the national pasttime once again and
No one was in the oval office
Giving head to the President.
America was standing tall.

Nothing ever is what it appears to be,
Not even our collective sanity.
As McGuire puts his ten-year-old son
Up in the air in enthusiastic joy,
No one, least of all the nervous sportscasters
Dares to ask where McGuire's ex-wife was.
No one wants to deal with it.

Popular Madness.
So many varieties that they are considering
A weekly magazine with the same title.
They can run specials on child murderers,
Militia members and special prosecutors who
Go about their business with the zeal
Of a Grand Inquisitor.

They can feature car bombers, or
Mail bombers, or cruise missile bombers
With rank, titles and apparent justification.
Apparent to whom?
They can run ads for homemade explosives
Made out of fertilizer and ivory soap.
Made out of the same crap they try to sell us on TV

(continued)

Popular Madness.
Buy it off the stands for $3.95 an issue or order your
Subscription today and save. Save, save, save!!!
Just bear in mind that one in a hundred
Of our magazines carries a small, harmless
Explosive inside.
Never enough to kill. Just enough to maim.

"Sixty-two home runs in a single season, quite a feat!"
Adds one of the fidgety announcers as McGuire rounds
The dirty bases.
Meanwhile a serial killer duct tapes up his latest prize
while trying to explain to her that his parents
never really understood him, and
Some punks from the south side do
A drive-by shooting somewhere along the north side.

Divorces soar, Russia collapses,
And nuclear devices cost a little less than a new BMW.
All this just as McGuire's right foot touches home plate.
Everything will be OK now that we have a new
Home-run king to distract us until
The next airplane goes down.
Or some drunk takes out a school bus.
Great magazine, by the way, Popular Madness.
I love the ads for land mines.

September, 1998

So what she is crazy

Woman is not whip.
Is not angel of braided straw.

Why then this attempt?
This cant display of luxury.

Why this when her warmest
flame is velvet.
　　　　Is innocence untorn.

So what she is crazy.
　　　Waiting the lover
　　　　she may never find.
For women as well are
caught in ethereal bondage.

She longs in medieval
desperation that the strings
　　　　shall never fail.

That the wind may never
　　　carry that much sand.

　　　　　　　Of the Blue Door Collection, 1975

God is a Good Mechanic

Did he not design me here
To this moment in time where I can write this hurried
Thank you note to him.
Praising him for another job well done,
Albeit thirty pounds heavier than the original blueprints and
Having a distinct propensity to swearing.

But should I not trust in his wisdom
Even at this?
Should not we, who see the world through
Lenses thick with our zealot's sense of arrogance,
Appreciate the skill with which
He had made the complex simple?
The simple complex?

Should we not
Appreciate the synchronized spin of a billion galaxies,
The blur of light, and
The improbable chemistry of organic molecules
That lay the very footings for this
Poem to pass from my fingertips
To your unspoken voice unscathed?

But why do we remain so standoffish?
So aloof in this often strained relationship.
Do we honestly think that we might have designed it
Better?
Are the lenses of our conceit so curved
To make us dare to think this foolishly?

(continued)

But there's the comedy
Within which we are caught like
Children in this guessing game of heaven.
For he has made us vain, and selfish for
That very reason.
You see, all he ever wanted was to have someone
To talk to.

So talk.

Winter, 2001

Zen is hell

My wings are numb
with explanation.
My mouth is
swollen with lies.
All of my legs refuse
to run.
My hands make carvings
of the idle.
My blood has changed to water...

(Fight is unflight.
Life is death.
Differences are
seen only by the blind.)

Heaven is Zen.

Birds of Paradise Collection, 1974

The Dance of Veils

We all lie to ourselves.
It isn't easy,
And often it is not by choice.
We are protecting the child within us from
The brutality of truth.

It is the dance of veils,
This deceit we become to our self.
The smoke-filled bar.
The arabesque music and the veils falling
Away like layers of skin.

We can lie to ourselves about our work,
About those we work with, saying
"What a wonderful group of people they are!"
While beneath that veil we wish
They would all politely rot in hell.

We can lie about our hobbies, our pastimes.
The clubs, the socials, the
Weekly meetings we attend with such enthusiasm
When we know there are times we want to
Take the podium and scream with rage.

We can lie about who we are, what we've done with
Our lives and our talents.
Cover for our cowardice with
Yet another veil, another thin piece of
Our human veneer.

(continued)

We can lie about whom we really love
and those whom we say we love.
We cover that lie the best,
Because within it we are vulnerable.
Hurtable. Defenseless.
It is here where we need these silken layers of deceit.

We can lie to God.
Both of us know it is the worst lie.
The thinnest veil, the most translucent design.
It is the same veil Peter knew in the garden.
Knowing that God can never lie to us.

But when the dance of veils is over. Skin gone,
And our nakedness laid out for all the world to see,
How we felt, who we really wanted to be.
Only then we will be standing there before that same God we
Cheated on.
And if we have the strength to
Forgive those who so deceived us,
He will forgive us our deceits.
The dance will cease
And the seedy patrons of this smoky bar will walk away
From the funeral parlor
Talking amongst themselves saying, "He was a fine man,"
"She was a good woman."
Some will mean it, some will not.
We all lie to ourselves, don't we?

July, 1995

The Wind Chimes

I was up late last night,
As sleepless as starlight.
The wind was light but noteworthy.
Without the wind chimes the breeze would have
Gone unnoticed. It would have slipped
Quietly by me.

Save for that small set of gift shop
Wind chimes that hang on the corner
Of the front porch. Hang silently when
The wind is calm,
And sing recklessly in a clamor of
Tubes and tin in a summer thunderstorm.

Last night their song was
Just a reminder, like breathing.
We never notice the air we breathe unless we
Think about it. In and out, keeping
This machine we are alive.
Keeping us quick.

Last night the wind chimes served to remind me
Of something I thought of long, long ago.
Sometimes life startles you into the
Mystical realm of itself,
And sometimes it nudges you,
Like a tiny prayer.

(continued)

Last night, amidst the fears and
Dislocations that come when
This restlessness overwhelms me,
So came the wind chimes.
Random songs in the
Darkness of an insecure night.
A private reminder of God.

Winter, 1999

Our Private Demons

I'm not asking you to name them.
You know their names as
Well as I do mine.
I'm not asking you to explain them.
They defy explanation.
Defiance is their strongest suit.
Just dance with them now and again.
Take them out of their shadowy closet and
Acknowledge them.
Let them put on their finest gown,
Pick them up at seven and take them to the ball.
Dance with them.
If you do not,
They will slow-waltz for years with
Your sweet sublime.
As horrid as that ball might be, the other cheek to cheek
Can turn your heart to stone and lay ruin your life
In painful pirouettes.
Do not misunderstand me.
They are rude, demanding and dangerous.
Their favorite party: the masquerade.
Their favorite dance: the tango.
Their favorite partner: the fool.
But to deny them is illusion.
Better to look them in the eye
While the music roars, and the room is
Alive with frivolity and fear,
And tell them face to face
The dance is over.
For now.

1995

Chant

It is the sound of sleep.
Of rhythms eternal.
The chant of surf.
How it soothes and becalms us.
A slow melody of waves and sand.
This oceanic whisper.

It is the song of the sea.
Curling. Uncurling.
Furling. Unfurling in primordial harmony.
How it wraps itself around us,
Embracing our souls in sweet allure.

It is the chorus Gregorian.
A thousand, thousand voices altogether
In this ceaseless chant of eternity.
Monks in deep blue robes singing
This whitecapped song of God.

It is the dream awakened.
The gentle hand of the ocean as if
Caressing the tired land.
Listen to it call to you.
Enthralling. Inviting. So alive.

(continued)

The chant goes on, and on, and on, and on
In perfect repetition.
Before these words gave it tribute and
Long since they will perish.
The chant of the surf washing against
The shorelines of this,
Our lonely Earth.

Six Mornings on Sanibel, 1996

Picture

My framework is weathered.
I no longer see with the focus of my eyes,
For what good is their
Cemented image in this furnace of change?

My vision is fat.
Pregnant with the blur of reality.
The picture is a jungle of
Distortion as
I have entered now into my own
Mythology. No longer hesitating at
The workings of human madness.

But instead, partaking in this
Bloodbath of the irrational.
Delighted
With this bent and wasted
Performance.

My framework is crooked
No longer taking firm hold of this picture
But twisted slightly more insanely
Toward the easier appraisal.
The images are thinner.
The world's innocence becomes only so much rust.
The world's guilt only
So much blame.

Winter, 1974

The Zipgun of Madness

The zipgun of madness aims at
neither heart nor limb,
but within
the head's soft matter ends.

No flesh wound does it trail
for skillful surgeon's hands to heal,
but seals all
entrances and then defends
its damage done
with the lunatic's keen eyes.
It watches and it waits in
quick demise.

The zipgun of madness
leaves a larger hole
than bandages can stuff.
It leaves enough
ill poison in the mind, to wind
away from cures.
And leave behind the sanity
we hold
to hold secure.

Birds of Paradise Collection, 1974

Of Peace on Earth

Everywhere guns pointing at each other,
and unbalanced me behind
triggers of discontent...

(when she moves slowly to me during
the pause of the dark
and wants reassurance.)

But armies, armed to the hilt,
with rifles hot from firing,
and children fleeing through alleyways
of death...

(while she asks me gently
what I believe?)

with all this ceaseless hatred
and bombing forever.
with so much worthless murdering
and blood pooled
upon this gigantic stone...

(and as I turn to answer her,
but before I am able
the Earth
falls back to sleep,
and night continues.)

Winter, 1971

This Morning the Sun Rose Upon My Grave

It pried open the lid on the coffin of night
To rise like some angel afire.
I was not afraid of it for I am dead.

In a forgotten chapter of Revelations, I found my soul
Stirring beneath its overwhelming light,
Wanting never to change an instant of my self, never to lie.

I saw all. The moment of my death,
The river of tears, the sound of their laughter
As my fabled stories were told and retold.

All life is in transit,
Like the sun that climbs atop the blue shoulders of the sky,
Like the sound of shovels filling this trench I'm forever in.

So we must take each second in earnest.
Breathe the last! Love the most intense!
Stretch our joys, our sorrows until they beg to snap!

We must never let passion fail us. Ever.
Or watch our lives be lost to limbo.
These things I say to you from my sun-drenched grave.

Too many the coward, too many the weak and undecided fools
Surround my rotting body in this eternity of dirt,
Daring never to write this hurried message to the living:

(continued)

"Venture forth! Today! At once! Put down this peasant's verse!
The sun it flies across the sky with the speed of light,
Catch it while you are filled with life. Revel in it.

"These things I know as tons of soil impound me.
Truths that will never fade. Be off this instant,
With your lovers and your life,
Grab the sunlight and dance
Upon my soon forgotten grave!"

The end of *Six Mornings on Sanibel*, Winter, 1995

Lyrics
(1973-1977)

Author's Notes

These lyrics were originally written and performed back in the mid-1970s. At the time, I was in a three-piece coffeehouse group that toured across much of the United States. The band was called *Easy Steam*, and our sound was similar to that of another popular group of the same era, *America.*

The band stayed together from late 1973 through early 1977. My good friend, Dennis Cosgrove, wrote most of the music, I wrote the majority of the lyrics and Rudy Lundahl, the lead guitarist, kept us from killing each other. It was a fantastic time in my life.

We played colleges from Savannah, to Twin Falls, Idaho to New York University. Our hair long, our libidos unbridled and our party meters at red line, those years with *Easy Steam* were unreal.

I have an unfinished manuscript about those crazed, Kerouac-inspired years sitting somewhere in the corner of my studio. Someday I hope to pick up the work, appropriately called *Constant Strangers*, and finish it. But for now, all you have are these lyrics.

Three of these songs appeared on an album, *Easy Steam*, recorded in 1976 just before the band disintegrated in a ball of flame and youthful angst. The album is long since out of print, the last remaining copies of the album selling years ago for $50 each to a private collector in Germany. I have no idea why.

A few of the islanders who looked over the manuscript of *Rhythm of the Tides* felt that I should include the music with these lyrics. I thought about it, but except for "Islands" and "Vanishing," the other two songs were originally written as poems and adapted by the band to be used as lyrics. If it helps, "Islands" is a delicate song done in three-quarter time written for my wife, Molly, while "Vanishing" has a simple melody not unlike a medieval English folk song.

Of the four songs, over the years that have passed since the demise of *Easy Steam*, "Vanishing" has now become my favorite.

Charles Sobczak
August, 2001

Birds of Paradise

I see the birds in your eyes.
Mouth melting into wing.
     Breath to paradise.
     Breath to paradise.
     Breath to paradise.
          I feel the wind of your voice.
          Words curved angelically,
          Songs soaring through
          Unlit hells.
               Soaring through hells.
               Soaring through hells.
               Soaring through hells.

And my apology
does not fly.
Instead stunned of whirling thoughts through the sky,
while your body becomes
dust with age.
     For you are crushed with age.
     Feathers stripped.
     Song drowned in this orgy
     of complaint.
Awkward.
Suffering.
Trying to find flight above the gnarled and hungry roots
of the human situation.

I see the birds in your eyes.
Mouth melting into wing.
     Breath to paradise.
     Breath to paradise.
     Breath to paradise.

Summer, 1975

Islands

Is it this simple, lying here with you.
Peaceable fantasia when our centuries are through.
When our centuries have released us,
Their imperatives, their divorce.
We flow toward this moment
Letting love choose the course.

Chorus:
      For we are an Island,
      Beneath feathered palms.
      Lovers in Eden.
      In the eye of the storm.

Away from the tempest, a collage of delight.
Romantically framed in Baudelaire's moonlight.
On beaches of diamonds, chant rhythms of surf,
While gracious and giving, flesh touches earth.

Chorus:
      For we are an Island,
      Beneath feathered palms.
      Lovers in Eden.
      In the eye of the storm.

Winter, 1978

Wall to Wall

And so it is they refuse to answer the door.
They refuse to
Pick up the murderous telephone.
They refuse to take in the mail,
Their distrust settled in
  like a rusted nail.

It soon becomes a game,
Where reason stalls and
Imagination wails...
  signal flares,
  frantic gestures,
  singing telegrams,
  bottled notes,
  books, mags,
  familiar quotes,
  newspapers,
  poems,
  songs,
  cable television,
  eventually
a rock lobbed through their
big bay window with a tiny note attached
asking them, *how does it feel to be alive?*

They just draw further and further back,
Penned up within themselves
Like fish drying in the sun.
Thank heaven the siege has just begun.

       Convolutions Collection, 1974

Vanishing

My thoughts, in smoke, do quickly vanish.
Between the answers held in air.
My life, it seems, will likewise follow.
That so, these footsteps disappear.

A man, it seems, is but a riddle.
A prince, a queen, or merely a pawn.
We learn so much, but know so little.
The wise man rests when his day is done.

Chorus:
>   For such is the motion where changes are worn.
>   Yesterday's mountains were yesterday born.
>   And such is the candle which brightens the dawn.
>   Yesterday's mountains are yesterday gone.

Each man must make it on his fortune,
Was written by a lonely hand.
We are, as all, as one together,
Like warmth is to this frozen land.

The beggar's bowl is never empty.
The future never heeds the past.
A balance, even if deceitful,
Remains so balanced.

(continued)

Chorus:
> For such is the motion where changes are worn.
> Yesterday's mountains were yesterday born.
> And such is the candle which brightens the dawn.
> Yesterday's mountains are yesterday gone.

1973